City of London Pa

A handlist of parish registers, register transcripts
and related records at Guildhall Library

Guildhall Library Publications

Seventh (Revised) Edition 1999

Cover illustration: Watercolour of monument to Sir Thomas Offley, Lord Mayor 1556, in St Andrew Undershaft. By Thomas Fisher, c.1810.

This watercolour appears on the Library's COLLAGE system. COLLAGE is an innovative image database, available on the Internet at **http://collage.nhil.com**, providing instant access to over 30,000 works of art from the Guildhall Library Print Room and Guildhall Art Gallery.

British Library Cataloguing in Publication Data.
A catalogue record for this book is available from the British Library

Corporation of London
Guildhall Library Publications
Guildhall Library
Aldermanbury
LONDON EC2P 2EJ

ISBN 0 900422 44 0

First published 1963
Seventh Edition 1999

Printed by Hobbs the Printers, Totton, Hampshire.

INTRODUCTION

This is the 7th, revised, edition of Guildhall Library's handlist of its source material relating to Anglican baptisms, marriages and burials in the City of London. It also includes the former parish of Holy Trinity Minories and the district chapelry of St Thomas in the Liberty of the Rolls which, although outside the City, are now united to City parishes. The parishes of St Andrew Holborn, St Botolph Aldersgate, St Botolph Aldgate, St Giles Cripplegate and St Sepulchre Holborn also cover some areas outside the City. A map showing boundaries of parishes within the City of London can be consulted in the Library.

This handlist describes material in the Library's custody at 1 May 1999. Material held elsewhere is mentioned if it contains relevant information not included in the Library's holdings. Additions of special interest since the 6th (1990) edition include:

- a full transcript by Library staff of the baptism register of St Dunstan in the East, 1813-1938. This register was damaged beyond repair by enemy action in 1941 and has hitherto been unavailable for use.
- five original register books and one banns book of Bridewell Chapel, formerly thought to have been destroyed by enemy action in 1940. These were rediscovered at King Edward's School, Witley, Surrey, in 1996.

GENERAL NOTES ON THE SOURCES

1. Parish registers.
   a. Although many parishes have lost their churches through demolition or destruction and have been united with other parishes, they often continued to maintain separate registers for many years after the date of the union. Details are given in the text.

   b. Under the City of London (Guild Churches) Act 1952, some City churches no longer have parochial status but have become guild churches to serve the non-resident population of the City. These churches still maintain their own registers.

   c. The term 'banns' is used in this handlist as a convenient description of the 'publications' of marriages which are found in parish registers during the Commonwealth period, as well as of conventional banns books of later date.

   d. Burials in City burial grounds were discontinued at various dates in the 1850s and no parish burial registers were maintained thereafter. Most subsequent burials took place at cemeteries outside the City, but the City parishes do not appear to have kept any record of where their parishioners were buried.

2. Marriage licences.
   Collections of marriage licences are to be found in some parish archives, and these are indicated in the text. There are also records connected with the issuing of licences: Guildhall Library holds London diocesan marriage allegations from

1597 and bonds from 1664, and Dean and Chapter of St Paul's Cathedral marriage allegations (covering the parishes of St Faith under St Paul, St Giles Cripplegate, St Gregory by St Paul and St Helen Bishopsgate) 1670-1841. London diocesan allegations 1521-1685 are held by London Metropolitan Archives, 40 Northampton Road, London EC1R 0HB. Similar series covering licences issued by the Archbishop of Canterbury are held by Lambeth Palace Library, London SE1 7JU.

3. Records of clandestine marriages.

   Before 1754 there were a number of London clergymen who performed marriages, generally without banns or licence, for people from all parts of the country who wished to be married in secrecy or with minimum delay. Many such marriages took place c.1644-c.1700 at Holy Trinity Minories and St James Duke's Place, *q.v.*

   From c.1667 large numbers of clandestine marriages were performed in the Fleet Prison chapel and in taverns, private houses and other buildings nearby. Details of source material for these 'Fleet marriages' are given in this handlist, under Fleet Prison and Old Red Hand and Mitre chapel.

4. Burial receipts.

   Account books of fees received for burials, giving the names of persons interred, are listed in the text. Such records of fees as are included in churchwardens' accounts are only listed if they cover a period for which no original burial register survives.

5. Monumental inscriptions.

   These provide another possible means of tracing burials for which no registers survive, or of obtaining information additional to that found in burial registers. This handlist does not list all the transcripts of inscriptions which are available in the Library: full details of these can be found in the London subject catalogues in the Printed Books and Manuscripts reading rooms, at L77.5.

6. Transcripts.

   Transcripts of registers, published and unpublished, are listed separately at the end of each parish entry in the handlist. References to transcripts are also given in the main part of the parish entry a) if the transcript includes an index, or b) if it covers any period for which original registers are not available in the Library.

7. Indexes.

   Indexes to individual registers and transcripts are indicated in the text. There are also various composite indexes covering the registers of a large number of parishes:

   a. The Mormon microfiche international genealogical index, or IGI (chiefly baptisms, with some marriages, c.1538-c.1880), compiled by the Church of Jesus Christ of Latter-Day Saints. The Library holds a copy of the entire index for the British Isles, including that part which covers many parishes and chapels in the City of

London and the former county of Middlesex. The index is known to be incomplete, but it has not been possible to ascertain the exact extent of its coverage. Users of the index are warned that the lists of parishes and dates given in the *Parish and Vital Records List* (Church of Latter-Day Saints) may not correspond precisely with the coverage of the current microfiche (i.e. that dated 1992), and that in some cases individual registers are not indexed comprehensively. This handlist indicates those City parishes for which a substantial number of entries are known to be included in the current microfiche. The 1993 CD-ROM version of the index for the British Isles, with its subsequent amendments, is also available in the Library's Printed Books Section. This version enables a search to be made for the whole of the British Isles in one operation, or by individual counties or groups of counties; it is also possible to search for children of a particular couple.

b. Boyd's marriage index (c.1538-c.1837), compiled c.1925-55 by Percival Boyd and subsequently by others. Full details of the Middlesex and London main series and the Second and Third (Miscellaneous) series are given, as appropriate, in the appendix to this handlist. A microfiche copy of the entire index, covering over 4000 parishes in England, is available in Guildhall Library Printed Books Section.

c. The Pallot index to marriages (c.1780-c.1837), held by Achievements Ltd., Northgate, Canterbury, Kent, CT1 1BA. A list giving details of the parishes and dates covered by this index can be consulted at Guildhall Library.

d. Boyd's burial index (c.1538-c.1853), compiled c.1934 by Percival Boyd. This is a selective index, i.e. it is not complete for any specific dates, parishes or surnames and covers males only. The entries are chiefly from the Cities of London and Westminster, with some from other parts of Greater London formerly in the counties of Middlesex and Surrey. A microfilm copy of this index is available in Guildhall Library Printed Books Section.

e. City of London burial index 1813-53 parts 1-3, compiled 1981-97 by Cliff Webb, John Hanson, Monnica Stevens and others. This is a complete index of burials 1813-53 in City of London parishes, plus Bridewell Chapel, Mercers' Hall Chapel and St Paul's Cathedral. Part 1 of the index (Webb 36) covers St Sepulchre Holborn only and up to 1857; part 2 (Webb 54/1-2) covers over 80 parishes in one alphabetical sequence of surnames; and part 3 (microfiches 104) covers the remaining parishes, including Bridewell Chapel, Mercers' Hall Chapel and St Paul's Cathedral, also in one alphabetical sequence of surnames. Copies of the three parts of the index are available in Guildhall Library Printed Books Section. Transcripts, with indexes, for each parish in part 3 have been deposited at the Society of Genealogists, 14 Charterhouse Buildings, Goswell Road, London EC1M 7BA.

Hannah Dunmow
Stephen Freeth
June 1999

ABBREVIATIONS

The following abbreviations are used:-

B tr	:	bishop's transcript(s)
Bap	:	baptism(s)
Boyd	:	Boyd's marriage index, Middlesex and London main series and Second and Third (Miscellaneous) series (available in GL Printed Books Section)
Bur	:	burial(s)
Challen	:	the series of register transcripts compiled by William Harold Challen, 1924-60 (available in GL Printed Books Section)
GL	:	Guildhall Library
HS	:	the series of register transcripts published by the Harleian Society register section (available in GL Printed Books Section)
IGI	:	international genealogical index
Mar	:	marriage(s)
Ms(s)	:	manuscript(s)
Reg	:	register(s)
Tr	:	transcript(s)
Webb	:	the series of register transcripts/indexes compiled by Clifford Reginald Webb, c.1973-95 (available in GL Printed Books Section). Note that vols 36 and 54/1-2 are part of the City of London burial index 1813-53 (see p v for details)

Most of the original registers described in this handlist may be consulted only on microfilm. The microfilms are readily available for consultation in the Manuscripts reading room at Guildhall Library. Copies from microfilms may be made, by personal callers only, using the microfilm reader/printer in the Manuscripts reading room.

ALLHALLOWS BARKING BY THE TOWER

Reg (bap from 1558, mar from 1564, bur from 1558) held by the Parish Clerk, Allhallows-by-the-Tower, Byward Street, London EC3R 5BJ (available on Monday afternoons only by written appointment; fee payable).

Tr and index of bap 1558-74/5: P.R.W. Blewett, *Allhallows by the Tower ... the parish registers, baptisms ...* (computer script, 1984), **GL Printed Books Section**.

Tr and index of mar 1564-74: P.R.W. Blewett, *Allhallows by the Tower ... the parish registers, marriages ...* (computer script, 1986), **GL Printed Books Section**.

B tr of bap, mar and bur 1800-1 and 1812, **Ms 11147**.

Bur 1813-53 indexed in J. Hanson and M. Stevens, *City of London burial index 1813-1853 part 3* (Milton Keynes, 1997?), fiches 104, **GL Printed Books Section**. Tr and index held by the Society of Genealogists, 14 Charterhouse Buildings, Goswell Road, London EC1M 7BA.

ALLHALLOWS BREAD STREET

United to St Mary le Bow, 1876

Partial index to bap in **IGI**.

Bap, mar (with St John the Evangelist Friday Street from c.1673) and bur 1538-1723, **Ms 5031**. Rough bap 1618/9-54, mar 1619-50, bur 1618/9-53/4, **Ms 5032** (with some variant entries). Indexes to Ms 5031: **Boyd** (mar); **in HS 43** (bap, mar and bur).

Bap 1723-1812, mar 1723-53 (with St John the Evangelist Friday Street), bur 1723-1812, **Ms 5033**. Rough bap and bur from 1789, **in Ms 5034** (with some variant entries, and some rough bap and bur of St John the Evangelist Friday Street). Indexes to Ms 5033: **Boyd** (mar); **in HS 43** (bap, mar and bur).

Bap 1813-92 (with St John the Evangelist Friday Street from 1821), **Ms 5035**. Rough bap to 1820, **in Ms 5034**. Index to Ms 5035: **in HS 43**.

For later bap see St Mary le Bow.

Mar 1754-1812 (with St John the Evangelist Friday Street), **Ms 5036/1**. Indexes: **Boyd; in HS 43**.

Mar 1813-37 (with St John the Evangelist Friday Street), **Ms 5036/2**. Indexes: **Boyd; in HS 43**.

Mar 1837-76 (with St John the Evangelist Friday Street), **Ms 10377**. Index: **in HS 43**.

Mar licences collection 1840-66 (with St John the Evangelist Friday Street), **Ms 5062**.

Bur 1813-51 (with St John the Evangelist Friday Street from 1822), **Ms 5037**. Rough bur to 1820, **in Ms 5034** (entries from 1815 record some details not found in **Ms 5037**). Indexes to Ms 5037: **in HS 43; in Webb 54/1-2**.

Later mar entered in reg of St Mary le Bow.

Transcripts:

Bap 1538-1892, mar 1538-1876, bur 1538-1851, **HS 43**. Indexed.

B tr of bap and bur 1813-16, **Ms 11239A**; bap 1817, 1819-36 and 1851-3, mar 1814-16 and 1819-36, bur 1817, 1819-36 and 1851 (all with St John the Evangelist Friday Street), **Ms 11239**. Note: b tr of bap, mar and bur 1799, 1802 and 1804-11 are held by Lambeth Palace Library, London SE1 7JU.

ALLHALLOWS HONEY LANE

United to St Mary le Bow, 1670

Partial index to bap and mar in **IGI**.

Bap 1538-1697, mar 1546-1656 and 1664-6, bur 1538-1666/7, **Ms 5022** (mar 1656/7-64 missing). Indexes: **Boyd** (mar); in **HS 44-5** (bap, mar and bur).

Bap 1697/8-1812, mar 1675-1812, banns 1754-1937, bur 1697/8-1812: see St Mary le Bow.

Bap 1813-92, **Ms 5023**. Indexes: **in HS 44-5** (to 1837); **in Webb 3** (bap 1838-92 of persons born before 1841).

For later bap see St Mary le Bow.

Mar 1818-36, **Ms 5024**. Indexes: **Boyd; in HS 45**.

Bur 1814-51, **Ms 5025**. Indexes: **in HS 44-5; in Webb 54/1-2**.

Later mar entered in reg of St Mary le Bow.

Transcripts:

Bap 1538-1697 and 1813-37, bur 1538-1666/7 and 1814-51, **HS 44**. Indexed in HS 45.

Mar 1546-1656, 1664-6 and 1818-36, **HS 45**. Indexed

Bap 1667/8-97, **in Ms 4997**.

B tr of bap, mar and bur 1800-2 and 1810 (from reg of St Mary le Bow with Allhallows Honey Lane), **Ms 11163**; bap 1817-36, 1838-46, 1848-56 and 1867, mar 1818-19 and 1825-36, bur 1818-35, 1838-45 and 1851, **in Ms 14565**.

ALLHALLOWS LOMBARD STREET

United to St Edmund the King and Martyr, 1937

Partial index to bap and mar in **IGI**.

Bap 1550/1-1653, mar 1553-1653, bur 1549/50-1653, **Ms 17613**. Index: **Boyd** (mar).

Bap 1653-1735, mar 1654-1734/5, banns 1654-62/3, bur 1653-98/9 and 1726-35, **Ms 17614**. One bap 1655 in **Ms 17613**. Index: **Boyd** (mar and banns).

Bap 1735-1812, mar 1735-53, bur 1735-1812, **Ms 17615**. Index: **Boyd** (mar).

Bap 1813-19, **Ms 17616**. Tr in Ms 17617.

Bap 1819-1937 (with St Benet Gracechurch and St Leonard Eastcheap from 1867 and with St Dionis Backchurch from 1877), **Ms 17617**. Includes tr of Ms 17616.

Mar 1754-1812, banns 1755-1817, **Ms 17618/1**. Index: **Boyd** (except banns 1776-1800).

Mar 1813-19, **Ms 11257**. Tr in Ms 17618/2. Index: **Boyd**.

Mar 1819-37, **Ms 17618/2**. Includes tr of Ms 11257. Index: **Boyd**.

Mar 1837-1937 (with St Benet Gracechurch and St Leonard Eastcheap from 1867 and with St Dionis Backchurch from 1877), **Ms 17619**.

Banns 1818-1937 (with St Benet Gracechurch and St Leonard Eastcheap from 1867 and with St Dionis Backchurch from 1877), **Ms 11258**. Index: **Boyd** (to 1837).

Bur 1813-19, **Ms 11259**. Tr in Ms 17620. Index: **in Webb 54/1-2**.

Bur 1820-53, **Ms 17620**. Includes tr of Ms 11259. Index: **in Webb 54/1-2**.

Later bap, mar and banns entered in reg of St Edmund the King and Martyr.

Transcripts:

Mar 1553-1837, banns 1654-62/3 and 1755-1837, **Challen 6**.

B tr of bap 1813-28 and 1830-46, mar 1813-37, bur 1813-46, **Ms 11241**. Note: b tr of bap, mar and bur 1799 and 1803-13 are held by Lambeth Palace Library, London SE1 7JU.

ALLHALLOWS LONDON WALL

Partial index to bap and mar in **IGI**.

Receipts for bur (with names of deceased) 1459-1536, in churchwardens' accounts, **in Ms 5090/1**. Index: in C. Welch, *The Churchwardens' Accounts of Allhallows London Wall* (privately printed; London, 1912), **GL Printed Books Section**.

Bap and mar 1559-1653, bur 1559-1651, **Ms 5083**. Bap 1585/6-95 and 1596/7-1604, mar 1570-1604/5, bur 1569/70-1604, also **in Ms 5084** (entries to 1598 record additional detail not found in Ms 5083; later entries are apparently identical to those in Ms 5083). Indexes: **Boyd** (mar); in E.B. Jupp and R. Hovenden, *The Registers ... of the parish of Allhallows London Wall* (privately printed; London, 1878), **GL Printed Books Section**.

Bap and mar 1653-75, bur 1653-74, **Ms 5085**. Indexes: **Boyd** (mar); in Jupp and Hovenden, as above, **GL Printed Books Section**.

Bap 1675-1729/30, mar 1675-92, bur 1675-1729/30, **Ms 5086**.

Mar 1692/3-1730, **Ms 5087**. Index: **Boyd** (from 1701).

Bap 1729/30-1812, mar 1730-54, bur 1729/30-1812, **Ms 5088**. Index: **Boyd** (mar).

Bap 1813-44, **Ms 5088A/1**.

Bap 1844-75, **Ms 5088A/2**.

Mar 1754-85, **Ms 5089/1**. Index: **Boyd** (to 1775).

Mar 1786-1812, **Ms 5089/2**. Index: **Boyd** (from 1801).

Mar 1813-32, **Ms 5089A/1**. Index: **Boyd**.

Mar 1833-7, **Ms 5089A/2**. Index: **Boyd**.

Mar 1837-1927, **Ms 5089A/3**.

Mar 1928-45, **Ms 5089A/4**.

Banns 1823-90, **Ms 5089B**. Index: **Boyd** (to 1837).

Bur 1813-49, **Ms 5088B**. Index: **in Webb 54/1-2**.

Later bap reg retained by incumbent.

Transcripts:

Bap and mar 1559-1675, bur 1559-1674, Jupp and Hovenden, as above, **GL Printed Books Section**. Indexed.

Mar 1675-1837, banns 1823-37, **Challen 23**.

B tr of bap, mar and bur 1629-30/1, **in Ms 10107**; 1639-39/40, **in Ms 10107A**; 1801-4, 1807-9 and 1811-12, **Ms 11153**; 1813-37, **Ms 11344**.

ALLHALLOWS STAINING

United to St Olave Hart Street, 1870

Partial index to bap and mar in **IGI**.

Receipts for bur (with names of deceased) in churchwardens' accounts 1491-1550, **in Ms 4956/1**; 1533-1628, **in Ms 4956/2** (includes some receipts for mar 1617-28); and 1645-1706, **in Ms 4956/3**.

Bap 1642-1710, mar and bur 1653-1710, **Ms 17824**. Indexes: **Ms 21584/1** (bap); **Boyd** (mar).

Bap 1710-43, mar 1710-40, bur 1710-28, in **Ms 17825**. Tr of bap **in Ms 17826/1**, with annotations made by transcriber (1794), from oral evidence. Additional bap 1729-44, not found in Ms 17825, transcribed from a vol apparently no longer extant, **Ms 17826A**. Indexes: **Ms 21584/2** (bap, from Ms 17826/l); **Boyd** (mar).

Bap 1744-57: reg not extant. Rough bap from 1746, **in Ms 17830**; transcribed **in Ms 17826/1**, with annotations made by transcriber (1794), from oral evidence. Index: **Ms 21584/2** (from Ms 17826/l).

Bap 1757-94, **Ms 17826/2** (indexed 1757-61). Rough bap 1746-62 and 1766, **in Ms 17830** (with some variant entries). Tr of Ms 17826/2, **in Ms 17826/1**, with annotations made by transcriber (1794), from Ms 17830 and from oral evidence. Index: **Ms 21584/2** (from Ms 17826/l).

Bap 1794-1812: reg not extant. Tr (contemporary) of bap for these dates, **in Ms 17826/1.** Rough bap from 1794 (July), **in Ms 4954** (entries to 1812 apparently identical to those in Ms 17826/l). Index: **Ms 21584/2** (from Ms 17826/l).

Bap 1813-70, **Ms 17826/3**. Rough bap to 1815, **in Ms 4954** (incomplete for 1813-15). Index: **Ms 21584/3** (from Ms 17826/3).

Mar 1740/1-54: reg not extant. Four mar 1748-50, **in Ms 17830**, and one mar 1753, **in Ms 17825** (all indexed in **Boyd**).

Mar 1754-80, **Ms 17827/1**.

Mar and banns 1780-1812, **Ms 17828**.

Mar 1813-37, **Ms 17827/2**.

Mar 1837-69, **Ms 17827/3**.

Banns 1824-70, **Ms 17829/2**.

Bur 1728/9-36: unrecorded.

Bur 1736-7, **in Ms 17825**.

Bur 1737/8-45: unrecorded.

Bur 1745/6-57: the only registrations appear to be in vol containing rough bur 1745/6-62, **Ms 17830**.

Bur 1757-1801, **Ms 4955**. Rough bur to 1762, **in Ms 17830** (some entries record, besides details in Ms 4955, ages of deceased).

Bur 1801-12, **in Ms 17831/1**. Includes tr of bur 1794-1801 from Ms 4955.

Bur 1813-53, **Ms 17831/2**. Index: **in Webb 54/1-2**.

For later bap, mar and banns see St Olave Hart Street.

Transcripts:

Bap 1642-1710, **Ms 21584/1**. Indexed.

Bap 1710-1812, **Ms 17826/1**. Tr **in Ms 21584/2** (indexed).

Bap 1813-70, **Ms 21584/3**. Indexed.

Mar 1653-1740, 1748-50 and 1753, **Challen 12**.

B tr of bap 1800-53, mar 1800-37, bur 1800-53, **Ms 11151**.

ALLHALLOWS THE GREAT

United to St Michael Paternoster Royal, 1893

Partial index to bap and mar in **IGI**.

Receipts for bur (with names of deceased) 1616-29, in churchwardens' accounts, **in Ms 818/1**.

Bap 1668-1720, mar 1671-1719/20 (with Allhallows the Less), bur 1666/7-1720, **Ms 5159**. Indexes: T.C. Dale and J.H. Mann, 'All Hallows the Great ... register of baptisms ...' (typescript, 1935), **GL Printed Books Section**; **Boyd** (mar); T.C. Dale, 'Marriages at All Hallows the Great and Less ...' (typescript, n.d.), **GL Printed Books Section**; T.C. Dale and J.H. Mann, 'All Hallows the Great ... register of burials ...' (typescript, 1937), **GL Printed Books Section**.

Bap 1720-65, mar 1720-22/3 and 1741/2-54 (with Allhallows the Less), bur 1720-65, **Ms 5161** (mar 1723-41 missing). Indexes: Dale and Mann, '...baptisms ...', as above, **GL Printed Books Section**; **Boyd** (mar); Dale, as above, **GL Printed Books Section** (mar); Dale and Mann, '... burials ...', as above, **GL Printed Books Section**.

Bap and bur 1765-1812, **Ms 5162**. Indexes: Dale and Mann, as above, **GL Printed Books Section** (bap and bur).

Bap 1813-56 (with Allhallows the Less), **Ms 5164/1**. Index: **in Webb 1** (1813-40).

Bap 1856-88 (with Allhallows the Less), **Ms 5164/2**.

Later bap entered in reg of St Michael Paternoster Royal.

Mar and banns 1754-99 (with Allhallows the Less), **Ms 5163/1.** Includes two undated banns (post-1799) and one banns dated 1818. Indexes: **Boyd** (mar to 1775); Dale, as above, **GL Printed Books Section** (mar).

Mar 1799-1812, banns 1799-1812 and 1814-23 (with Allhallows the Less), **Ms 5163/2**. Indexes: **Boyd** (mar from 1801); Dale, as above, **GL Printed Books Section** (mar).

Mar 1813-37 (with Allhallows the Less), **Ms 5163/3**. Indexes: **Boyd**; Dale, as above, **GL Printed Books Section**.

Mar 1837-90 (with Allhallows the Less), **Ms 5163/4**.

Banns 1823-89 (with Allhallows the Less), **Ms 9302**.

Mar licences collection 1813-97 (with Allhallows the Less), **Ms 9307/2**. Index: **in Ms 24657** (to 1838).

For later mar, banns and mar licences see St Michael Paternoster Royal.

Bur 1813-48 (with Allhallows the Less), **Ms 5165/1**. Indexes: **in Webb 54/1-2**; T.C. Dale and J.H. Mann, 'All Hallows the Less (jointly with All Hallows the Great 1813-1853) register of burials ...' (typescript, 1936), **GL Printed Books Section**.

Bur 1848-53 (with Allhallows the Less), **Ms 5165/2**. Indexes: **in Webb 54/1-2**; Dale and Mann, '... jointly with All Hallows the Great ... burials ...', as above, **GL Printed Books Section**.

Transcripts:

Bap 1668-1812, Dale and Mann, 'All Hallows the Great ... register of baptisms ...' (typescript, 1935), **GL Printed Books Section**. Indexed.

Mar 1671-1722/3 and 1741/2-54, **Challen 9**.

Bur 1666/7-12 Dale and Mann, 'All Hallows the Great ... register of burials ...' (typescript, 1937), **GL Printed Books Section**. Indexed.

Bap 1813-40, bap 1841-69 of persons born before 1841, **Webb 1**. Indexed.

Bap 1819-21 and 1823, bur 1819-20, **Ms 5165A**.

Bur 1813-53, in Dale and Mann, 'All Hallows the Less (jointly with All Hallows the Great 1813-1853) register of burials ...' (typescript, 1936), **GL Printed Books Section**. Indexed.

B tr of bap, mar and bur 1800-4 and 1807-12, **Ms 11148**; bap 1813-52, 1854-6 and 1858-65, mar 1813-52, 1854-9 and 1861-4, bur 1813-48 (all with Allhallows the Less), **Ms 11242**; bap 1867 (with Allhallows the Less), **Ms 9316**.

Index to mar 1671-1837, Dale, 'Marriages at All Hallows the Great and Less ...' (typescript, n.d.), **GL Printed Books Section**.

ALLHALLOWS THE LESS

United to Allhallows the Great, 1670; St Michael Paternoster Royal, 1893

Partial index to bap and mar in **IGI**.

Bap 1558-1654, mar 1558-1653, bur 1558-1654, **Ms 5160/1**. Indexes: T.C. Dale and J.H. Mann, 'All Hallows the Less ... register of baptisms ...' (typescript, 1933), **GL Printed Books Section**; **Boyd** (mar); T.C. Dale, 'Marriages at All Hallows the Great and Less ...' (typescript, n.d.), **GL Printed Books Section**; T.C. Dale and J.H. Mann, 'All Hallows the Less ... register of burials ...' (typescript, 1936), **GL Printed Books Section**.

Bap 1655-1812, mar 1655-66, bur 1655-1812, **Ms 5160/2**. Indexes: Dale and Mann, '... baptisms ...', as above, **GL Printed Books Section**; **Boyd** (mar); Dale, as above, **GL Printed Books Section** (mar); Dale and Mann, '... burials ...', as above, **GL Printed Books Section**.

For later reg see Allhallows the Great.

Transcripts:

Bap 1558-1812, Dale and Mann, 'All Hallows the Less ... register of baptisms ...' (typescript, 1933), **GL Printed Books Section**. Indexed.

Mar 1558-1666, **Challen 9**.

Bur 1558-1812, Dale and Mann, 'All Hallows the Less ... register of burials ...' (typescript, 1936), **GL Printed Books Section**. Indexed.

B tr of bap, mar and bur 1629-30/1, **in Ms 10107**; 1639-39/40, **in Ms 10107A**; 1800-4 and 1807-12 (including mar from reg of Allhallows the Great with Allhallows the Less), **Ms 11149**.

Index to mar 1558-1666, Dale, 'Marriages at All Hallows the Great and Less ...' (typescript, n.d.), **GL Printed Books Section**.

ALL SAINTS SKINNER STREET

District chapelry constituted 1864; united to St Botolph Bishopsgate, 1869

Bap 1858-67, **Ms 21142**.

Mar 1864-9, **Ms 21143**.

BRIDEWELL CHAPEL

Hospital and precinct church; united to St Bride Fleet Street, 1864

Note: the entry for this chapel has been heavily revised since the rediscovery in 1996 at King Edward's School, Witley, Surrey, of five register books and one banns book, all previously thought to have been destroyed by enemy action in 1940. These books appear below as Mss 8310/3, 8312/3-4 and 33401-3.

Partial index to bap in **IGI**.

B tr of bap, mar and bur 1665-6, **in Ms 10952**. Index to mar: **in Webb 17 and 40**.

Bap 1669/70-82, mar 1671-81, bur 1666/7-81/2, **Ms 8309**, now largely illegible following damage by enemy action in 1940. Tr (compiled before reg was damaged), **Ms 33404/1**. Index to mar: **Boyd**.

Bap, mar and bur 1682-93/4, **Ms 8310/1**. Indexes to mar: **Boyd**; **in Webb 17 and 40**.

Bap 1695-1742, mar 1694-1742, bur 1695-1742, **Ms 8310/2**. Indexes to mar: **Boyd** (1701-25); **in Webb 17 and 40**.

Bap 1742-1812, mar 1741/2-54, bur 1742-1812, **Ms 8310/3,** now largely illegible and unfit for production following damage by enemy action in 1940. Rough bap 1742-1812, mar 1742-54 and bur 1742-1812, **in Ms 8311/2;** rough bap and bur 1750-75, **in Ms 8311/1** (bur entries record fees paid). Index to mar (from Ms 8311/2): **in Webb 17 and 40**.

> Note: Ms 8310/3 was rediscovered in Surrey in 1996. The present Ms 8311/2 appears in previous editions of this *Handlist* as Ms 8310/3, but has since been recatalogued as a rough register, not the fair copy.

Bap 1813-63, **Ms 33401**. Rough bap 1820-2 and bap accounts 1821-46, **in Ms 8311/2** (most entries less detailed than those in Ms 33401).

Mar 1754-1801, **Ms 8312/1**, now largely illegible following damage by enemy action in 1940. Rough mar 1754-77, **in Ms 8311/1** (with many variations from entries in Ms 8312/1). Tr of one mar 1787 and one mar 1799 (made from sources compiled before Ms 8312/1 was damaged), **Ms 18609/1**. Ms 8312/1 and Ms 8311/1 are transcribed, collated and indexed **in Webb 17 and 40**.

Mar 1802-18, **Ms 8312/2**, now largely illegible following damage by enemy action in 1940. Tr of mar 1802-9 (made from sources compiled before Ms 8312/2 was damaged), **Ms 18609/2**. B tr of mar 1815 and 1818, **in Ms 11243**. Ms 8312/2 and mar in Ms 11243 are transcribed, collated and indexed **in Webb 17 and 40**.

Mar 1822-37, **Ms 8312/3**. Mar accounts 1822-37, **in Ms 8311/2** (some entries differ from those in Ms 8312/3). Mar in Mss 8311/2 and 11243 (b tr) are transcribed, collated and indexed **in Webb 17 and 40**.

Mar 1838-63, **Ms 8312/4**. Mar accounts 1838-47, **in Ms 8311/2** (some entries differ from those in Ms 8312/4).

Banns 1757-1862, **Ms 33402**.

Bur 1813-45, **Ms 33403**. Bur accounts 1820-45, **in Ms 8311/2** (some entries differ from those in Ms 33403). Index (from b tr): in J. Hanson and M. Stevens, *City of London burial index 1813-1853 part 3* (Milton Keynes, 1997?), fiches 104, **GL Printed Books Section**.

For bap, mar and banns from 1864, and mar licences from 1869, see St Bride Fleet Street.

Transcripts:

Mar 1665-6 and 1682-1818 (from reg, except for Mss 8310/3 and 8312/3, not then rediscovered; also from rough reg and/or b tr, for those years for which the original reg is illegible), **in Webb 17**. Index: **in Webb 17** (places) **and 40** (names).

Bap 1669/70-98, mar 1671-93 and bur 1666/7-93 (compiled before reg was damaged), **Ms 33404/1**.

One mar 1787 and one mar 1799 (made from sources compiled before reg was damaged), **Ms 18609/1**.

Mar 1802-9 (made from sources compiled before reg was damaged), **Ms 18609/2**.

Mar 1822-37 (from mar accounts and b tr), **in Webb 17**. Index: **in Webb 17** (places) **and 40** (names).

B tr of bap, mar and bur 1665-6, **in Ms 10952**; bap 1813-16, 1818-44, 1846-54, 1856-63, mar 1815, 1818, 1822-5 and 1828-37, bur 1813-16 and 1818-44, **Ms 11243**.

CHRISTCHURCH NEWGATE STREET (also known as CHRISTCHURCH GREYFRIARS)

United to St Sepulchre Holborn, 1954

Partial index to bap and mar in **IGI**.

Note: this parish was formed in 1547, in the place of the parishes of St Ewin and St Nicholas Shambles which were dissolved. The church of the former monastery of the Friars Minor, or Grey Friars, became the parish church of the new parish. Bur in this church 1275-c.1540 are recorded in British Library Ms Cotton Vitellius F. XII, pars 14, ff 273-315, transcribed and printed by E.B.S. Shepherd, 'The Church of the Friars Minor in London', *Archaeological Journal*, vol 59 (1902), pp 266-87; also transcribed, with annotations, by J.C.C. Smith, **Ms 9264A**.

Bap, mar and bur 1547-88, **Ms 9264**. Includes bap, mar and bur at St Nicholas Shambles 1538-47. Indexes: **Boyd** (mar); **in HS 21** (bap, mar and bur).

Bap 1588-1656, mar and bur 1588-1666: reg probably destroyed in the Great Fire. Bur accounts 1593-6, **in Ms 9163**. B tr of bap, mar and bur 1639-39/40, **in Ms 10107A** (mar indexed **in Webb 16 and 40**).

Bap 1656/7-1724, mar 1667-1837, bur from 1666 (all with St Leonard Foster Lane from c.1670): reg destroyed by enemy action in 1940. The following sources are available:

> Tr and index of bap 1656/7-1754, mar 1667-1754, bur 1666-1754, **in HS21**. Mar to 1754 also indexed in **Boyd**.
>
> Tr of extracts from bap 1656/7-1812, mar 1667-1778, bur 1666-1812, held by the Archivist, College of Arms, Queen Victoria Street, London EC4V 4BT (in Chester Ms 48; available by appointment only).
>
> Tr of extracts from bap 1669-1877, mar 1676-1928, bur 1667-1853, **in Ms 3713/1**.
>
> Tr of extracts from mar 1758 and 1778 and bur 1756-1806, **in Ms 21660**.
>
> Some mar c.1780-1837 in the Pallot Index, held by Achievements Ltd., Northgate, Canterbury, Kent CT1 1BA.
>
> Some b tr exist for the years 1800-36 (incomplete): see list below.

Bap 1724-1812 (with St Leonard Foster Lane), **Ms 21649**, now partly illegible following damage by enemy action in 1940. Transcribed and indexed to 1754 **in HS 21**. Tr of extracts, 1757-96, **in Ms 21660**.

Bap 1813-24 (with St Leonard Foster Lane), **Ms 9545/1**. Rough bap 1813-19, **in Ms 9546/1**, and from 1819, **in Ms 9546/2** (entries apparently identical to those in Ms 9545/1).

Bap 1824-1940 (with St Leonard Foster Lane), **Ms 9545/2**. Rough bap to 1825, **in Ms 9546/2** (entries apparently identical to those in Ms 9545/2). Rough bap 1831-2, **in Ms 9546/3**, 1832-67, **in Ms 9546/4**, and 1867-81, **in Ms 9546/5** (some entries omitted; others apparently identical to those in Ms 9545/2).

Mar 1837-1940 (with St Leonard Foster Lane), **Ms 8951**, 5 vol.

1. 1837-9	3. 1843-8	5. 1863-1940.
2. 1839-43	4. 1849-63	

Banns 1870-1923 (with St Leonard Foster Lane), **Ms 8915/1**, now partly illegible following damage by enemy action in 1940.

Banns 1924-40 (with St Leonard Foster Lane), **Ms 8915/2**.

B tr of bap, mar and bur 1800-36 (incomplete; all with St Leonard Foster Lane except where indicated):-

Bap 1800-2, mar 1800-1, bur 1800 and 1802 (Christchurch only), **Ms 10114A/1**.
Mar 1802 (Christchurch only), **Ms 10114A/2**.
Bap mar and bur 1800-2 (St Leonard only), **in Ms 10412**.
Bap mar and bur 1804, **Ms 10115/1**.
Bap and bur 1807 (Apr.)-1808 (Dec.) (Christchurch only), **Ms 10114A/3**.
Mar 1807 (Apr.)-1808 (Apr.) (Christchurch only), **Ms 10114A/4**.
Mar 1808 (Apr.-Dec.) (Christchurch only), **Ms 10114A/5**.
Bap, mar and bur 1808(Jan.-Dec.) (St Leonard only), **in Ms 10412**.
Bap, mar and bur 1809-36, **Ms 10115/4-31**, 28 vol.

4. 1809	11. 1816	18. 1823	25. 1830
5. 1810	12. 1817	19. 1824	26. 1831
6. 1811	13. 1818	20. 1825	27. 1832
7. 1812	14. 1819	21. 1826	28. 1833
8. 1813	15. 1820	22. 1827	29. 1834
9. 1814	16. 1821	23. 1828	30. 1835
10. 1815	17. 1822	24. 1829	31. 1836

Index to bur (1813-36): in J. Hanson and M. Stevens, *City of London burial index 1813-1853 part 3* (Milton Keynes, 1997?), fiches 104, **GL Printed Books Section**.

Transcripts:

Bap 1538-88 and 1656/7-1754, mar 1538-88 and 1667-1754, bur 1538-88 and 1666-1754, **HS 21**. Indexed. Note: this vol contains many inaccuracies and omissions, some of which are noted by J. Challenor Smith in *The Genealogist*, N. S. vol 12 (1896), pp 223-5.

Mar 1639-39/40 (from b tr), **Webb 16**. Index: **in Webb 16** (places) **and 40** (names).

For b tr see lists above.

FLEET PRISON, AND RULES OF THE FLEET

Partial index to bap and mar in **IGI**.

Reg of clandestine mar c.1667-1754 (833 vol; also including some bap) performed in the Fleet Prison and the Rules of the Fleet are held by the Keeper of Public Records, Public Record Office, Kew, Surrey TW9 4DU (P.R.O. class RG7). An additional reg 1724/5-30/1 is held by the Keeper of Western Manuscripts, Bodleian Library, Oxford OX1 3BG (Ms Rawlinson B.360). For further details see Introduction.

The following are available at GL:

Index to some mar 1691/2-1702 (i.e. to those entered in the reg numbered RG7/833), S.W. Prentis, 'Fleet Marriages 1691/2-1702' (typescript, 1962), **GL Printed Books Section**.

Tr of extracts from mar 1709-54, in J.S. Burn, *The Fleet Registers ...* (London, 1833), **GL Printed Books Section**. Also contains extracts from mar at the Mint, Southwark, 1718-26, which are included in the Fleet reg. Indexed in **Boyd**, which also contains a small number of other Fleet mar, not found in Burn, c.1667-1754.

Tr and index of some mar 1736 (Nov.)-1754 (Jan.) (i.e. to those entered in the reg numbered RG7/118 and RG7/162), M. Herber, *Clandestine marriages in the chapel and rules of the Fleet Prison ...* (London, 1998), **GL Printed Books Section**.

See also Old Red Hand and Mitre chapel.

GUILDHALL CHAPEL (non-parochial)
Demolished 1822

No reg of this chapel are known to exist; and none are recorded in the *Parish register abstract* of the 1831 census. Possibly no separate reg were maintained (cf. *Notes and Queries*, 9th series, vol 1, p 317).

Two mar 1620 and 1639, in reg of St Michael Bassishaw, **in Ms 6986** and **Ms 6987**.

Mar 1668/9-1701/2 and bur 1669-77, in reg of St Lawrence Jewry, **in Ms 6975**. Index: **Boyd** (mar 1668/9-84/5).

Monumental inscriptions 1671-1763, **Ms 2879**. Tr by B. Lloyd (typescript, 1978), **GL fo pam 4339**.

HOLY SEPULCHRE WITHOUT NEWGATE:- see ST SEPULCHRE HOLBORN

HOLY TRINITY GOUGH SQUARE
District chapelry constituted 1842; united to St Bride Fleet Street, 1906

Partial index to bap and mar in **IGI**.

Bap 1842-82, **Ms 6571/1**. Index: **in Webb 3** (bap of persons born before 1841).

Bap 1882-1906, **Ms 6571/2**. Index: **in Webb 3** (bap of persons born before 1841).

Mar 1869-1906, **Ms 6604**.

Banns 1879-1906, **Ms 6605**.

For later reg see St Bride Fleet Street.

HOLY TRINITY MINORIES
United to St Botolph Aldgate, 1893

Partial index to bap in **IGI**.

Bap 1563-1717, mar 1579/80-1644, bur 1566-1714, **Ms 9238** (bap and bur entries from 1710 record numbers of days interval between birth and bap, and between death and bur; for tr of these entries (bap from 1710, bur from 1712), omitting number of days interval, but for bap entries recording actual dates of birth, see Ms 9239 below). Index to mar: **Boyd**.

Bap 1717-1812, bur 1714-50, **Ms 9239**. Includes tr of bap 1710-17 and bur 1712-14 from Ms 9238.

Bap 1813-97, **Ms 9240**.

Mar 1644-48/9, **Ms 9241/1**. Index: **Boyd**.

Mar 1657/8-59, **Ms 9242A**. Index: **Boyd**.

Mar 1660-3, **Ms 9241/2**. Index: **Boyd**.

Mar 1676-83, **Ms 9242B**. One mar 1679 **in Ms 9245**. Tr and index to Ms 9242B: **Ms 23491/1**.

Mar 1683-1754, entered in three vol, **Mss 9243-5,** as follows:

Mar 1683-6/7 and 1692-1754, **Ms 9243**. Indexes: in vol (1683-6/7 and 1692-1705, males only); **Ms 23491/2 and 4-5** (1683-6/7 and 1692-1754).

Mar 1686/7-92, **Ms 9244**. Index: **Ms 23491/3**.

Mar 1693/4-1713, **Ms 9245** (many entries in this vol are abbreviated versions of those in Ms 9243).

Mar 1754-1898, **Ms 9246**, 5 vol.

1. 1754-1812
2. 1813-28
3. 1828-37
4. 1837-60
5. 1860-98.

Banns 1754-1898, **Ms 9946**, 5 vol.

1. 1754-98
2. 1798-1824
3. 1824-6 and 1829-44*
4. 1826-7 and 1844-52
5. 1852-98.

*Includes tr of banns 1823-4 from Ms 9946/2.

Bur 1750-1812, **in Ms 9242**. Indexed (A-H at back, I-Z at front).

Bur 1813-52, **Ms 9247**. Index: **in Webb 54/1-2**.

For later bap and mar see St Botolph Aldgate.

Transcripts:

Mar 1644-8 and 1657/8-63, **in Ms 9242**.

Mar 1676-83, **Ms 23491/1**.

B tr of bap, mar and bur 1629-29/30, **in Ms 10107**; bap, mar and bur 1638-38/9, **in Ms 10952**; bap, mar and bur 1639-39/40, **in Ms 10107A**; bap 1801-4 and 1808-48, mar 1801-4 and 1808-37, bur 1800-4 and 1808-48, **Ms 11342**.

HOLY TRINITY THE LESS

United to St Michael Queenhithe, 1670; St James Garlickhithe, 1875

Partial index to bap in **IGI**.

Bap 1547-1653, mar 1547-1653 and 1657-63, bur 1547-1653, **Ms 9155**. Index: **Boyd** (mar).

Bap 1653-1716/7, mar 1653-58/9 and 1663/4-66, bur 1653-1729/30, **Ms 9156**. Rough bap and bur 1695, **in Ms 9153/1**. Index: **Boyd** (mar).

Bap 1717-1812, bur 1730-1812, **Ms 9157**.

Bap 1813-36, **Ms 9158**.

Mar 1670-1753: for main series of registrations, see St Michael Queenhithe. Three mar 1694-6 and one mar 1730, **in Ms 9156**. Index: **Boyd**.

Mar and banns 1754-1812 (with St Michael Queenhithe 1795-1812), **Ms 9159/1**. Index: **in Webb 16 and 40**.

Mar 1813-30, **Ms 9159/2**. Index: **in Webb 16 and 40**.

Bur 1813-52, **Ms 9161**. Index: **in Webb 54/1-2**.

For later bap, mar and banns see St Michael Queenhithe.

Transcripts:

Mar 1547-1666, 1694-6 and 1730, **Challen 27**.

Mar 1754-1830, banns 1754-1812, **Webb 16**. Index: **in Webb 16** (places) **and 40** (names).

B tr of bap, mar and bur 1629-30/1, **in Ms 10107**; 1639-39/40, **in Ms 10107A**; 1800-5 and 1807-19, **Ms 11524**. For later b tr see St Michael Queenhithe.

LAMB'S CHAPEL, MONKWELL STREET (non-parochial)

Also known as St James in the Wall; demolished 1872

Bap 1620/l-27, mar 1618/9-26, 1640, 1688 and 1696-8, **Ms 1159/1**. Tr: **in Webb 4**. Indexes: **in Webb 4** (bap); **Boyd** (mar).

Mar 1709-53, **Ms 1159/2**. Tr and index: **in Webb 4.**

MERCERS' HALL CHAPEL (non- parochial)

Partial index to mar in **IGI**.

Mar 1592 and 1683/4-84, bur 1563-1666, in reg of St Mary Colechurch, **in Ms 4438**.

Mar 1683/4-84 also in reg of St Mildred Poultry, **in Ms 4429/1**.

Bur 1671-1715, in reg of St Mary Colechurch, **in Ms 4439**.

Reg of mar 1641-1754 and bur 1640-1833 held by the Keeper of Public Records, Public Record Office, Kew, Surrey TW9 4DU. Available on microfilm at the Family Records Centre, 1 Myddelton Street, London EC1R 1UW. Indexes: mar 1701-54 in **Boyd**; bur 1814-44 in J. Hanson and M. Stevens, *City of London burial index 1813-1853 part 3* (Milton Keynes, 1997?), fiches 104, **GL Printed Books Section**.

Later registrations (20th century) have been entered in the reg of St Mary le Bow. A copy of these registrations is held by the Mercers' Company, Mercers' Hall, Ironmonger Lane, London EC2V 8HE.

OLD RED HAND AND MITRE CHAPEL (non-parochial)

This 'chapel' was one of the places in the vicinity of the Fleet Prison where clandestine marriages were performed: for further details see Introduction. The reg of the chapel, containing bap 1751-3 and mar 1750-4, was held at St Martin Ludgate until 1929, when it was deposited at the General Register Office. It is now held by the Public Record Office, Kew, Surrey TW9 4DU (P.R.O. reference RG7/256).

Tr of bap 1751-3, mar 1750-4, **Challen 12**.

ST ALBAN WOOD STREET

United to St Vedast Foster Lane, 1954

Partial index to bap and mar in **IGI**.

Reg to 1662 not extant (presumed destroyed by enemy action in 1940). The following sources are available:

> Receipts for bur (with names of deceased) in churchwardens' accounts 1584-1636, **in Ms 7673/1**; 1636-57 and 1661-75, **in Ms 7673/2**. Index: **in Webb 106**.
>
> Tr of extracts from bap 1591-1623, mar 1572, bur 1600 and 1617, in J.P. Malcolm, *Londinium Redivivum* (London, 1803), vol 2, pp 310-11, **GL Printed Books Section**. Index: **in Webb 106**.
>
> B tr of bap, mar and bur 1629-29/30, **in Ms 10107**. Index: **in Webb 106**.

Bap 1662/3-1786, mar 1662/3-1754 (with St Olave Silver Street from 1681), bur 1662/3-1786, **Ms 6527**. Index: **in Webb 106**.

Later bap reg destroyed by enemy action in 1940. B tr of bap 1800-12, **in Ms 11150**; 1813-27 (with St Olave Silver Street), **in Ms 11150A/1**; 1828-52 (with St Olave Silver Street), **in Ms 11150A/2**. Index: **in Webb 106**.

Mar 1754-1811 (with St Olave Silver Street), **Ms 6528**. Index: **in Webb 106**.

Mar 1811-1902: reg destroyed by enemy action in 1940. B tr of mar 1811-12, **in Ms 11150**; 1813-27 (with St Olave Silver Street), **in Ms 11150A/1**; 1828-36 (with St Olave Silver Street), **in Ms 11150A/2**. Indexes: **in Webb 106**; some mar c.1800-37, in the Pallot Index, held by Achievements Ltd., Northgate, Canterbury, Kent CT1 1BA.

Mar 1903-34 (with St Olave Silver Street, St Michael Wood Street and St Mary Staining), **Ms 6529**.

Bur 1786-1849: reg destroyed by enemy action in 1940. B tr of bur 1800-12, **in Ms 11150**; 1813-27 (with St Olave Silver Street), **in Ms 11150A/1**; 1828-49 (with St Olave Silver Street), **in Ms 11150A/2**. Rough bur 1840-9 (with St Olave Silver Street), **Ms 1261** (omitting names of officiating ministers, but recording dates of death and fees paid). Indexes: to Mss 11150 and 11150A/1-2, **in Webb 106** (1800-49); Ms 11150A/1-2 also indexed **in Webb 54/1-2**.

Transcripts:

Bap 1629-29/30, 1662/3-1786 and 1800-52, mar 1629-29/30 and 1662/3-1836, bur 1629-29/30 and 1662/3-1786 (from reg; also from b tr for those years for which no original reg survives), **Webb 11**. Index: **in Webb 106**.

Bur 1800-49 (from b tr), **Webb 12**. Index: **in Webb 106**.

B tr of bap, mar and bur 1629-29/30, **in Ms 10107**; bap, mar and bur 1800-12, **Ms 11150**; bap, mar and bur 1813-27 (with St Olave Silver Street), **Ms 11150A/1**; bap 1828-52, mar 1828-36, bur 1828-49 (all with St Olave Silver Street), **Ms 11150A/2**. Index: **in Webb 106**.

ST ALPHAGE LONDON WALL

United to St Giles Cripplegate, 1954

Partial index to bap and mar in **IGI**.

Receipts for bur (with names of deceased) in churchwardens' accounts 1527-53, **in Ms 1432/1**; 1553-80, **in Ms 1432/2**; 1580-1630/1, **in Ms 1432/3**.

Bap and mar 1613-99, bur 1613-78, **in Ms 5746/1**. Indexes to mar: **in Ms 5753; in Webb 102**.

Bur 1678-99: not extant.

Bap, mar and bur 1699-1732, **Ms 5746/2**. Rough bap 1699-1713 and mar 1699-1720, **in Ms 5746/1** (bap entries apparently identical to those in Ms 5746/2; mar entries omit addresses). Indexes to mar: **in Ms 5753; in Webb 102**.

Bap 1732-1812, mar 1732-54, bur 1732-1812, **Ms 5746/3**. Indexes to mar: in **Ms 5753**; **in Webb 102**.

Bap 1813-1920, **Ms 5750**.

Mar and banns 1754-1807, **Ms 5747/1**. Rough banns from 1803, **in Ms 5749/1**. Indexes to mar: **in Ms 5753; in Webb 102**.

Mar 1807-12, banns 1807-15, **Ms 5747/2**. Rough banns for these dates, **in Ms 5749/1**. Indexes to mar: **in Ms 5753; in Webb 102**.

Mar 1813-36, **Ms 5748/1**. Indexes: **in Ms 5753**; **in Webb 102**.

Mar 1837-1916, **Ms 5748/2**. Index: **in Ms 5753** (to 1868).

Banns 1815-80, **in Ms 5749/2**. Rough banns to 1823, **in Ms 5749/1**.

Banns 1852-5, **in Ms 11452** (duplicating the entries in Ms 5749/2, and additionally recording addresses and dates of mar).

Banns 1882, **in Ms 11452**.

Banns 1885, **in Ms 5749/1**.

Banns 1911, **in Ms 5749/2**.

Bur 1813-51, **Ms 5751**. Index: **in Webb 54/1-2**.

For later reg see St Mary Aldermanbury (which served as the parish church of the parish of St Alphage London Wall from 1917 to 1953).

Transcripts:

Mar 1613-1836, **in Webb 102**. Indexed.

B tr of bap, mar and bur 1629-29/30, **in Ms 10107**; bap, mar and bur 1639-39/40, **in Ms 10107A**; bap, mar and bur 1800-1 and 1803-12, **Ms 11159**; bap 1813-40 and 1842-9, mar 1813-36, bur 1813-40 and 1842-9, **Ms 11159A**.

Index to mar 1613-1868, **Ms 5753**.

ST ANDREW BY THE WARDROBE

Partial index to bap and mar in **IGI**.

Bap 1558-1812, **Ms 4502/1**.

Bap 1813-1939, **Ms 4502/2**.

Mar 1558-1725, **Ms 4503**.

Mar 1726-73 (with St Ann Blackfriars), **Ms 4504/1**. Indexed 1754-73.

Mar 1773-1812 (with St Ann Blackfriars), **Ms 4504/2**. Indexed 1773-87.

Mar 1813-40, **Ms 4505**.

Mar 1841-52 (with St Ann Blackfriars), **Ms 4506/1**. Includes tr of mar 1837-40 from Ms 4505 (St Andrew) and Ms 4509/2 (St Ann).

Mar 1852-75 (with St Ann Blackfriars), **Ms 4506/2**.

Mar 1875-1940 (with St Ann Blackfriars), **Ms 4506/3**.

Affidavits for publication of banns 1822-3 (with St Ann Blackfriars), **Ms 9204**.

Banns 1824-45 (with St Ann Blackfriars), **Ms 4506A**.

Mar licences collection 1712-1889 (with St Ann Blackfriars), **Ms 2101**, 4 boxes. Index: **in Ms 24657** (to 1838).

Bur 1558-1812, **Ms 4507/1**.

Bur 1813-50, **Ms 4507/2**. Index: in J. Hanson and M. Stevens, *City of London burial index 1813-1853 part 3* (Milton Keynes, 1997?), fiches 104, **GL Printed Books Section**.

Later bap and mar reg retained by incumbent.

Transcripts:

B tr of bap and mar 1800-05, 1807-24, 1826-43 and 1845-52 (mar with St Ann Blackfriars from 1841), bur 1800-05, 1807-24, 1826-43 and 1845-49, **Ms 11154**.

ST ANDREW HOLBORN

Partial index to bap in **IGI**.

Bap 1558-1889, **Ms 6667**, 29 vol.

1. 1558-1623	9. 1724-39/40	17. 1815-17	25. 1836-41
2. 1623-42	10. 1739/40-61	18. 1817-18	26. 1841-49
3. 1642-54	11. 1761-70	19. 1818-20	27. 1849-58
4. 1654-76	12. 1771-80	20. 1820-21	28. 1858-69
5. 1676-93	13. 1781-92	21. 1821-24	29. 1869-89
6. 1693-1704	14. 1792-1805	22. 1824-28	
7. 1704-17	15. 1805-12	23. 1828-31	
8. 1717-24	16. 1813-15	24. 1831-36	

Mar 1559-1698, **Ms 6668/1**. Banns and mar 1653-8, **Ms 6668/5** (including some mar not found in Ms 6668/1, but omitting others recorded there).

Mar 1698-1714: reg not extant. Tr (contemporary) of mar for these dates, **in Ms 6668/2**.

Mar 1714-20, **Ms 6669**.

Mar 1720-36, **Ms 6668/3**.
Mar 1736-54, **Ms 6668/4**.

Mar 1754-1812, entered in two concurrent series, for mar by banns and for mar by licence, as follows:

Mar by banns, **Ms 6670**, 11 vol.

1. 1754-58	4. 1769-75	7. 1787-93	10. 1806-12
2. 1758-64	5. 1775-81	8. 1793-1800	11. 1812
3. 1764-69	6. 1781-87	9. 1800-06	

Mar by licence, **Ms 6671**, 8 vol.

1. 1754-57	3. 1763-68	5. 1774-81	7. 1790-1802
2. 1757-63	4. 1768-74	6. 1781-90	8. 1802-12

Mar 1813-1952, **Ms 6672**, 35 vol.

1. 1813-15	10. 1840-41	19. 1854-56	28. 1875-78
2. 1815-17	11. 1841-43	20. 1856-58	29. 1878-82
3. 1817-20	12. 1843-44	21. 1858-60	30. 1882-87
4. 1820-21	13. 1844-46	22. 1860-62	31. 1887-92
5. 1822-27	14. 1846-48	23. 1862-64	32. 1892-1903
6. 1827-32	15. 1848-49	24. 1864-66	33. 1903-21
7. 1832-37	16. 1849-51	25. 1866-69	34. 1921-34
8. 1837-38	17. 1851-53	26. 1869-72	35. 1934-52
9. 1838-40	18. 1853-54	27. 1872-75	

Banns 1754-8, **Ms 6675**.

Rough banns 1754-62, **Ms 6676**.

Banns 1862-93 and 1900-53, **Ms 6677**, 7 vol.

1. 1862-68	3. 1881-93	5. 1907-15	7. 1928-53
2. 1868-81	4. 1900-07	6. 1916-28	

Bur 1558-1723/4, **Ms 6673**/1-8, 8 vol.

1. 1558-1623	3. 1642-53	5. 1672-87/8	7. 1698-1715/6
2. 1623-42	4. 1653-72	6. 1688-98*	8. 1715/6-23/4

*Bur 1695-96 also entered **in Ms 6667/6**.

Bur 1723/4-26, **in Ms 6667/8**.

Bur 1726-1855, **Ms 6673**/9-21, 13 vol.

9. 1726-39	13. 1785-1802	17. 1819-23	21. 1849-55
10. 1739-55	14. 1802-12*	18. 1823-31	
11. 1755-68	15. 1813-16*	19. 1831-38	
12. 1768-85	16. 1816-19	20. 1838-49	

*Bur accounts 1812-15, **Ms 6678** (recording places of interment).

Index: (1813-55) in J. Hanson and M. Stevens, *City of London burial index 1813-1853 part 3* (Milton Keynes, 1997?), fiches 104, **GL Printed Books Section**.

Later bap and mar reg retained by incumbent.

Transcripts:

Mar 1698-1720, **Ms 6668/2**.

B tr of bap, mar and bur 1639-39/40, **in Ms 10107A**; bap, mar and bur 1833, **Ms 6674/1**; bap, mar and bur 1834, with bur 1835 (Oct.-Nov.), **Ms 6674/2**.

ST ANDREW HUBBARD

United to St Mary at Hill, 1670

Partial index to bap and mar in **IGI**.

Bap 1538-99 and 1600/1, mar and bur 1538-99, **in Ms 1278/1** (bound up with vestry minutes 1600-78: bap at front, mar after minutes 1653, bur after minutes 1662). Index to mar: **Boyd**.

Bap 1600-1706, mar 1600-1754, bur 1600-1706: no reg for these years appears to survive, although it is possible that mar 1672-1754 are among those entered in the reg of St Mary at Hill (Ms 4546), where the parish of origin of the parties is not stated. One bap 1600/1, **in Ms 1278/1**. Bap, mar and bur 1621-22/3, **in Ms 1279/3** (bap pp 459-60, mar p 669, bur pp 841-2 [immediately following p 669]). B tr of bap, mar and bur 1639-39/40, **in Ms 10107A**. Receipts for bur (with names of deceased) 1639-53, in churchwardens' accounts, **in Ms 1279/3**. Index: **Boyd** (mar to 1622).

Bap and bur 1706-90, **Ms 4550**. Duplicate bap and bur 1742-90, in reg of St Mary at Hill, **in Ms 4546**.

Bap and bur 1790-1812: see St Mary at Hill.

Bap 1813-1988: see St Mary at Hill.

Rough bap 1822-5 and bur 1796-1825: see St Mary at Hill.

Mar 1754-1812: see St Mary at Hill.

Mar 1815-37, **Ms 23813**. Index: **in Webb 102**.

Later mar reg not deposited at GL. B tr of mar 1846, **in Ms 10431A**.

Banns 1824-1921: see St Mary at Hill.

Bur 1813-46, **Ms 4551**. Index: **in Webb 54/1-2**.

Transcripts:

Mar 1538-99 and 1621-22/3, **Challen 27**.

Mar 1639-39/40 (from b tr), **Webb 16**. Index: **in Webb 16** (places) **and 40** (names).

Mar 1815-37, **in Webb 102**. Indexed.

B tr of mar 1639-39/40, **in Ms 10107A**; bap, mar and bur 1800-5 and 1807-12, **Ms 11152**; bap 1813-44 and 1846, mar 1813-37 and 1846, bur 1813-44 and 1846 (all with St Mary at Hill), **Ms 10431A**.

ST ANDREW UNDERSHAFT

Partial index to bap in **IGI**.

Bap, mar and bur 1558-1634, **Ms 4107/1**.

Bap, mar and bur 1634-92, **Ms 4107/2**.

Bap 1692-1770, mar 1692-1753, bur 1692-1770, **Ms 4107/3**. Rough bap 1742-64, mar 1743-53, bur 1742-74, **Ms 4114** (bap and mar entries apparently identical to those in Ms 4107/3; some bur entries record details not found in Ms 4107/3). Index: **Boyd** (mar from 1726).

Bap and bur 1771-1812, **Ms 4108**. Rough bur to 1774, **in Ms 4114** (some entries record details not found in Ms 4108).

Bap 1813-46, **Ms 4110/1**.

Bap 1847-1901, **Ms 4110/2**.

Later bap reg retained by incumbent.

Mar 1754-65, banns 1754-60, **in Ms 4109/1**. Index: **Boyd**.

Mar 1765-92, banns 1764-85, **Ms 4109/2**. One mar 1779, **in Ms 4109/1**. Index: **Boyd** (to 1775).

Mar 1792-1812, banns 1792-1814, **Ms 4109/3**. Index: **Boyd** (from 1801).

Mar 1813-37, **Ms 4111/1**. Index: **Boyd**.

Mar 1837-1970, **Ms 4111/2**.

Banns 1824-51, **Ms 4113/1**. Index: **Boyd** (to 1837).

Banns 1852-1969, **Ms 4113/2**.

Mar licences collection 1836-58, **Ms 4150**. Index: **in Ms 24657** (to 1838).

Mar licences collection 1908-70, **Ms 24356**.

Bur 1813-49, **Ms 4112**. Index: **in Webb 54/1-2**.

Transcripts:

Mar 1558-1837, banns 1754-60, 1764-85, 1792-1814 and 1824-37, **Challen 37**. Another copy, **Ms 24355**.

B tr of bap, mar and bur 1639-39/40, **in Ms 10107A**; 1800-12, **Ms 11156**; 1813-27, 1829-30 and 1833-5, **Ms 11156A**.

ST ANN BLACKFRIARS
United to St Andrew by the Wardrobe, 1670

Partial index to bap in **IGI**.

Bap 1560-1700, **Ms 4508/1**.

Bap 1701-1812, **Ms 4508/2**.

Bap 1813-61, **Ms 4508/3**.

Later bap reg retained by incumbent of St Andrew by the Wardrobe.

Mar 1562-1726, **Ms 4509/1**.

Mar 1726-1812: see St Andrew by the Wardrobe.

Mar 1813-40, **Ms 4509/2**.

Banns 1716/7-24, **Ms 3603** (incomplete).

For later mar, and for banns 1822-45 and mar licences 1712-1889, see St Andrew by the Wardrobe.

Bur 1566-1700, **Ms 4510/1**. Rough bur 1689-89/90, 1691-91/2, 1697-8 and 1699-99/1700, **Ms 3837** (with some variations from entries in Ms 4510/1).

Bur 1701-1812, **Ms 4510/2**.

Bur 1813-49, **Ms 4510/3**. Index: in J. Hanson and M. Stevens, *City of London burial index 1813-1853 part 3* (Milton Keynes, 1997?), fiches 104, **GL Printed Books Section**.

Transcripts:

B tr of bap, mar and bur 1629-30/1, **in Ms 10107**; bap, mar and bur 1639-39/40, **in Ms 10107A**; bap 1800-5, 1807-11, 1813-24, 1826-43 and 1845-52, mar 1800-5, 1807-11, 1813-24 and 1826-40, bur 1800-5, 1807-11, 1813-24, 1826-43 and 1845-9, **Ms 11155**. For b tr of mar 1841-3 and 1845-52 see St Andrew by the Wardrobe.

ST ANNE AND ST AGNES

United to St Vedast Foster Lane, 1954

Partial index to bap and mar in **IGI**.

B tr of bap, mar and bur 1629-29/30, **in Ms 10107**.

Bap 1640-89, mar 1641/2-96, bur 1640-90, **Ms 6764/1**. Includes selective mar entries 1696 (June)-1697; for complete mar reg from June 1696, see Ms 6764/2. Index: **in Ms 6772A**, 12 vol, for which see list below.

Bap 1689-1734, births 1696-1711, mar 1696-1734, bur 1690-1734, **Ms 6764/2**. Index: **in Ms 6772A**, 12 vol, for which see list below.

Note: entries in Ms 6764/2 are in disorder - see note at front of vol concerning arrangement of contents.

Bap 1734/5-1812, mar 1734-54, bur 1734/5-1812, **Ms 6764/3**. Rough bap and bur 1788-92, **in Ms 6773A** (some entries omitted; others apparently identical to those in Ms 6764/3). Rough bap and bur 1796-8, **in Ms 6773B** (entries apparently identical to those in Ms 6764/3). Index to Ms 6764/3: **in Ms 6772A**, 12 vol, for which see list below.

Bap 1813-1924 (with St John Zachary from 1896), **Ms 6765**. Indexes: in reg; also (to 1837) **in Ms 6772A**, 12 vol, for which see list below.

Mar 1754-84, **Ms 6766/2**. Index: **in Ms 6772A**, 12 vol, for which see list below.

Mar 1784-1812, **Ms 6766/3**. Index: **in Ms 6772A**, 12 vol, for which see list below.

Mar 1813-37, **Ms 6766/4**. Index: **in Ms 6772A**, 12 vol, for which see list below.

Mar 1837-1938 (with St John Zachary), **Ms 11530**.

Banns 1774-94 (with St John Zachary), **Ms 1618/1**.

Banns 1795-9 (with St John Zachary), **Ms 1618/2**.

Banns 1824-1920 (with St John Zachary), **Ms 6773**.

Mar licences collection 1831-1937 (with St John Zachary), **Ms 11959**. Index: **in Ms 24657** (to 1838).

Bur 1813-53, **Ms 6767**. Indexes: **in Ms 6772A** (to 1837), 12 vol, for which see list below; **in Webb 54/1-2**.

Transcripts:

Bap and bur 1640-1780, **in Ms 6768**.

Bap 1640-1734, **Ms 3701/35**. Index: **in Ms 3701A/14** (A-J) and **in Ms 3701A/15** (K-Z).

Mar 1641/2-1721, **Ms 3701/34**. Index: **in Ms 3701A/14** (A-J) and **in Ms 3701A/15** (K-Z).

Mar 1722-34, **Ms 3701/39**.

Mar 1734-54, **Ms 3701/37**.

Mar 1641/2-1774, **Ms 6766/1**.

Bur 1640-1734, **Ms 3701/33**. Index: **in Ms 3701A/14** (A-J) and **in Ms 3701A/15** (K-Z).

B tr of bap, mar and bur 1629-29/30, **in Ms 10107**; bap, mar and bur 1665-6, **in Ms 10952**; bap 1800-1, 1807-22 and 1824-50, mar 1800-1 and 1807-37, bur 1801 and 1807-50, **Ms 11157**.

Indexes 1640-1837, **Ms 6772A**, 12 vol.

1. Bap 1640-1734 and 1813-37, A-C
2. Bap 1640-1734 and 1813-37, D-H
3. Bap 1640-1734 and 1813-37, I-O
4. Bap 1640-1734 and 1813-37, P-Z
5. Mar 1641/2-1837, A-F

6. Mar 1641/2-1837, G-P
7. Mar 1641/2-1837, Q-Z
8. Bur 1640-1734 and 1813-37, A-C
9. Bur 1640-1734 and 1813-37, D-H
10. Bur 1640-1734 and 1813-37, I-R
11. Bur 1640-1734 and 1813-37, S-Z
12. Bap and bur 1734/5-1812, A-Z.

ST ANTHOLIN BUDGE ROW
United to St Mary Aldermary, 1873

Partial index to bap and mar in **IGI**.

Bap, mar and bur 1538/9-1740/1 (mar with St John the Baptist Walbrook from c.1670), **Ms 9016**. Indexes: **Boyd** (mar); **in HS 8** (bap, mar and bur).

Bap 1740/1-1812, mar 1740/1-54 (with St John the Baptist Walbrook), bur 1740/1-1812, **Ms 9017**. Indexes: **Boyd** (mar); **in HS 8** (bap, mar and bur to 1754); **in Webb 7** (bap and bur from 1754).

Bap 1811-24 (also one entry 1775) and one mar 1750 (all with St John the Baptist Walbrook), **Ms 23312**.

Bap 1813-72 (with St John the Baptist Walbrook), **Ms 9018**. Index: **in Webb 7** (to 1840).

Mar and banns 1754-99 (both with St John the Baptist Walbrook), **Ms 9019/1**. Three mar 1758 also entered **in Ms 9017**. Index: **in Webb 7** (mar).

Mar 1799-1812, banns 1799-1847 (both with St John the Baptist Walbrook), **Ms 9019/2**. Index: **in Webb 7** (mar).

Mar 1813-37 (with St John the Baptist Walbrook), **Ms 9019/3**. One mar 1819 also entered **in Ms 9019/2**. Index: **in Webb 7**.

Mar 1837-73 (with St John the Baptist Walbrook), **Ms 9019/4**.

Banns 1847-1952 (with St John the Baptist Walbrook, and including banns published at St Mary Aldermary after closure of the church of St Antholin in 1873), **in Ms 8998**.

Bur 1813-53 (with St John the Baptist Walbrook), **Ms 9020**. Indexes: **in Webb 54/1-2**; **in Webb 7** (to 1837); **in Webb 3** (1838-53).

For later bap and mar, and for mar licences from 1874, see St Mary Aldermary.

Transcripts:

Bap, mar and bur 1538/9-1754, **HS 8**. Indexed.

Bap 1754-1840, bap 1841-69 of persons born before 1841, mar and bur 1754-1837, **Webb 7**. Indexed.

Bur 1838-53, **Webb 3**. Indexed.

B tr of bap, mar and bur 1800-2 and 1807-12 (mar 1800, 1802 and 1807-12 with St John the Baptist Walbrook), **Ms 11158**; bap, mar and bur 1813-14 and 1816-36 (all with St John the Baptist Walbrook), **Ms 11158A**.

ST AUGUSTINE WATLING STREET

United to St Mary le Bow, 1954

Partial index to bap and mar in **IGI**.

Bap, mar and bur 1559-1653, **Ms 8872/1**. Index: **Boyd** (mar).

Bap, mar and bur 1653-98 (mar with St Faith under St Paul from c.1674), **Ms 8872/2**. Some mar 1690-90/1 and 1695-8 also entered **in Ms 8884** (in abbreviated form, but some entries also record names of officiating ministers omitted from Ms 8872/2). Reg of affidavits of bur in woollen 1678-80, **in Ms 8873**. Index: **Boyd** (mar).

Bap 1698-1737, mar 1698-1720 (with St Faith under St Paul), bur 1698-1731, **Ms 8872/3**. Two mar 1698 also entered **in Ms 8884**. Reg of affidavits of bur in woollen 1730-1, **in Ms 8873**. Index: **Boyd** (mar).

Bap 1737-1812, affidavits of bur in woollen 1730-1, bur 1731-1812, **in Ms 8873**. Two rough bur 1750, **in Ms 8872/3**. Two rough bap 1812, **in Ms 8894/2**.

Bap 1813-1925 (with St Faith under St Paul from 1910), **Ms 8877**. Rough bap 1813-18, **in Ms 8894/2** (some entries omitted; others apparently identical to those in Ms 8877).

Mar 1720-54 (with St Faith under St Paul), **Ms 8874**. Index: **Boyd**.

Mar and banns 1754-74 (both with St Faith under St Paul), **Ms 8875/1**. Index: **Boyd**.

Mar 1774-1812, banns 1774-1805 (both with St Faith under St Paul), **Ms 8875/2**. Index: **Boyd** (except 1776-1800).

Mar 1813-36, **Ms 8876**. Index: **Boyd***.

*Some mar 1813-37, indexed in Boyd as entries in the reg of St Augustine Watling Street, are actually to be found in the reg of St Faith under St Paul (Ms 8887).

Mar 1837-1940 (with St Faith under St Paul), **Ms 8876A**.

Banns 1824-1940 (with St Faith under St Paul), **Ms 8879**.

Bur 1813-53, **Ms 8878**. Rough bur 1803-53, **in Ms 25742**. Index to Ms 8878: **in Webb 54/1-2**.

Transcripts:

Mar 1559-1837, banns 1754-1805, **Challen 13**.

B tr of bap, mar and bur 1629-30/1, **in Ms 10107**; bap, mar and bur 1800-01, 1807 and 1809-12, **Ms 11160**; bap 1813-45, mar 1813-36, bur 1813-45, **Ms 11346**.

ST BARTHOLOMEW BY THE EXCHANGE

United to St Margaret Lothbury, 1839

Partial index to bap and mar in **IGI**.

Bap 1558-1711/2, mar 1558/9-1706, bur 1558-1678 and 1706-11, **Ms 4374/1**. Index: **Boyd** (mar).

Mar 1706-12: reg not extant.

Bur 1678-1706: reg not extant. Receipts for bur (with names of deceased) 1703-4, in churchwardens' accounts, **in Ms 4383/2**.

Bur 1706-11, **in Ms 4374/1**.

Bap, mar and bur 1712-23: reg not extant. Rough bap, mar and bur for these dates, **in Ms 4374/2**. Index: **Boyd** (mar).

Bap 1723/4-1812, mar 1723/4-54, bur 1723/4-1812, **Ms 4375**. Rough bap, mar and bur to 1736/7, **in Ms 4374/2**. Rough bap 1736/7-1812, mar 1736/7-54, bur 1736/7-1812, **Ms 4376**. Entries in both rough mss apparently identical to those in Ms 4375. Index: **Boyd** (mar).

Bap 1813-40, **in Ms 4378**.

Mar 1754-1812, banns 1754-1811, **Ms 4377**. Index: **in Webb 16 and 40** (mar).

Mar 1813-37, **Ms 4379/1**. Index: **in Webb 16 and 40**.

Mar 1837-40, **Ms 4379/2**.

Banns 1811-40 (rough), **Ms 4381**.

Banns 1813-27 (fair), **Ms 4382**.

Bur 1813-38, **Ms 4380**. Index: **in Webb 54/1-2**.

For later reg and for mar licences collection from c.1841 see St Margaret Lothbury.

Transcripts:

Mar 1558/9-1706 and 1712-54, **Challen 8**.

Mar 1754-1837, **Webb 16**. Index: **in Webb 16** (places) **and 40** (names).

B tr of bap, mar and bur 1800-12, **Ms 10428**; bap, mar and bur 1814-32, **Ms 11349**; bap 1840, **Ms 4378A**.

ST BARTHOLOMEW MOOR LANE
Parish constituted 1850; united to St Giles Cripplegate, 1900

Partial index to bap in **IGI**.

Bap 1850-1901, **Ms 6426**, 3 vol.
1. 1850-4 2. 1854-86 3. 1886-1901.
Index to bap of persons born before 1841: **in Webb 3**.

Mar 1850-99, **Ms 6427**, 5 vol.
1. 1850-8 3. 1865-72 5. 1882-99.
2. 1858-65 4. 1872-82
Banns 1882-91, **Ms 6201/1**.

Banns 1892-9. **Ms 6201/2**.

For later reg see St Giles Cripplegate.

ST BARTHOLOMEW THE GREAT

Partial index to bap and mar in **IGI**.

Bap, mar and bur 1616-47, **Ms 6777/1**. Index: **Ms 6783/1**.

Bap 1647-81, mar 1647-1716, bur 1647-77, entered in two vol, **Ms 6777/2-3**, with some overlapping, as follows:

Bap 1647-54/5 and 1673-81, mar 1647-54 and 1660/1-1716, bur 1647-54/5 and 1665-77, **Ms 6777/2**. Index: **Ms 6783/2**.

Bap 1653-72/3 (with dates of birth 1653-60), mar 1653-60/1, bur 1653-65, **Ms 6777/3**. Index: **Ms 6783/3**.

Bur accounts (with names of deceased) 1649-99, **Ms 6506/1** (incomplete).

Bap 1681-1715/6, **Ms 6778/1**. Index: **in Ms 6783/4.**

Births of non-conformists' children 1695-1710, **in Ms 6780**. Index: **in Ms 6783/9**.

Bap 1716-72, **Ms 6778/2**. Index: **in Ms 6783/4**.

Bap 1773-1812, **Ms 6778/3**. Index: **in Ms 6783/6**.

Bap 1813-43, **Ms 6778/4**. Rough bap 1835-43, **Ms 6778A** (entries apparently identical to those in Ms 6778/4). Index to Ms 6778/4: **in Ms 6783/7**.

Bap 1843-93, **Ms 6778/5**. Index: **in Ms 6783/8**.

Bap 1893-1926, **Ms 6778/6**.

Later bap reg retained by incumbent.

Mar 1716-54, **Ms 6779/1**. Index: **in Ms 6783/5**.

Mar and banns 1754-72, **Ms 6779/2**. Index: **in Ms 6783/6** (mar).

Mar and banns 1773-86, **Ms 6779/3**. Index: **in Ms 6783/6** (mar).

Mar 1786-1812, banns 1786-1805, **Ms 6779/4**. Index: **in Ms 6783/7** (mar).

Mar 1813-1934, **Ms 6779**/5-9, 5 vol.

5. 1813-27
6. 1827-37
7. 1837-63
8. 1863-1914
9. 1914-34.

Indexes: **in Ms 6783/7** (1813-27); **in Ms 6783/8** (1827-1914).

Later mar reg retained by incumbent.

Banns 1805-29, **Ms 6782**.

Banns 1829-1906 and 1946-69, **Ms 20769/1**.

Banns 1906-46, **Ms 20769/2**.

Rough banns 1850-8, **Ms 20770**. Rough banns 1859-69, **Ms 6782A**.

Bur 1678-1715/6, **in Ms 6780**. Bur accounts (with names of deceased) to 1699, **in Ms 6506/1**, and from 1699/1700, **in Ms 6506/2** (both incomplete). Index to Ms 6780: **in Ms 6783/9**.

Bur 1716-82, **Ms 6781/1**. Bur accounts (with names of deceased) to 1769, **in Ms 6506/2** (incomplete). Index to Ms 6781/1: **in Ms 6783/5**.

Bur 1782-1812, **Ms 6781/2**. Index: **in Ms 6783/6**.

Bur 1813-43, **Ms 6781/3**. Indexes: **in Ms 6783/8**; in J. Hanson and M. Stevens, *City of London burial index 1813-1853 part 3* (Milton Keynes, 1997?), fiches 104, **GL Printed Books Section**.

Bur 1843-53, **Ms 6781/4**. Indexes: **in Ms 6783/8; in Webb 54/1-2**; in Hanson and Stevens, as above, **GL Printed Books Section**.

Transcripts:

B tr of bap, mar and bur 1665-6, **in Ms 10952**; bap, mar and bur 1807-24, **Ms 11343/1**; bap 1825-64, mar 1825-37, bur 1825-54, **Ms 11343/2**.

Indexes 1616-1914, **Ms 6783**, 9 vol.

1. Bap, mar and bur 1616-47
2-3. Bap 1647-81, mar 1647-1716, bur 1647-77
4. Bap 1681-1772
5. Mar 1716-54, bur 1716-82
6. Bap 1773-1812, mar 1754-86, bur 1782-1812
7. Bap 1813-43, mar 1786-1827
8. Bap 1843-93, mar 1827-1914, bur 1813-53
9. Bur 1678-1715/6, non-conformist births 1695-1710.

ST BARTHOLOMEW THE LESS

Partial index to mar in **IGI**.

Reg (from 1547) held by the Archivist, St Bartholomew's Hospital, West Smithfield, London EC1A 7BE (available by appointment only).

The following are available at GL:

Tr and index of bap 1547-1894, mar 1547-1837, banns 1754-1941, bur 1547-1848: M. Spearman (reproduction of typescript held by the Society of Genealogists; 1992), fiches 75, **GL Printed Books Section**.

Tr of mar 1547-1837, **Challen 52**.

Index of bur 1813-53 **in Webb 54/1-2**.

B tr of bap, mar and bur 1629-30/1, **in Ms 10107**; 1639-39/40, **in Ms 10107A**; 1807-12 (Jan.) and 1812 (May)-1813, **Ms 10411**.

ST BENET FINK

United to St Peter le Poer, 1842; St Michael Cornhill, 1906

Partial index to bap and mar in **IGI**.

Bap 1538-1719/20, mar 1538/9-1719, bur 1538/9-1653, **Ms 4097**. Dates of birth 1653-62, **in Ms 4098**. Index to Ms 4097: **Boyd** (mar).

Bap 1720-1812, mar 1720-54, **Ms 4099**. Index: **Boyd** (mar).

Bap 1813-28, **Ms 4102/1**.

Bap 1828-45, **Ms 4102/2**.

Mar 1754-1812, **in Ms 4100/1**. Index: **Boyd** (except 1776-1800).

Mar 1813-28, **Ms 4100/2**. Index: **Boyd**.

Mar 1829-36, **Ms 4100/3**. Index: **Boyd**.

Mar 1838-45, **Ms 4100/4**.

Banns 1653-62 and 1699-1715, **in Ms 4098**. Index: **Boyd**.

Banns 1754-1812, **in Ms 4100/1**. Index: **Boyd** (except 1776-1800).

Banns 1813-45, **Ms 4101**. Index: **Boyd** (to 1836).

Mar licences collection 1796-1845, **Ms 5423**. Index: **in Ms 24657** (to 1838).

Bur 1653-1812, **in Ms 4098**.

Bur 1813-28, **Ms 4103/1**. Index: **in Webb 54/1-2.**

Bur 1828-45, **Ms 4103/2**. Index: **in Webb 54/1-2**.

For later reg see St Peter le Poer.

Transcripts:

Mar 1538/9-1845, banns 1653-62, 1699-1715 and 1754-1845, **Challen 7**.

B tr of bap, mar and bur 1639-39/40, **in Ms 10107A**; bap 1800-2, 1804-18, 1821-34 and 1845, mar 1800-2, 1804-18 and 1821-34, bur 1800-2, 1804-18, 1821-34 and 1845, **Ms 10435**. For b tr from 1846 see St Peter le Poer.

ST BENET GRACECHURCH

United to Allhallows Lombard Street, 1864; St Edmund the King and Martyr, 1937

Partial index to bap and mar in **IGI**.

Receipts for bur (with names of deceased) 1548-1653, entered under 'receipts extraordinary' in churchwardens' accounts, **in Ms 1568**.

Bap 1558/9-1730, mar 1558-1730 (with St Leonard Eastcheap from 1705), bur 1558-1730, **Ms 5671**. Index to mar: **Boyd**.

Bap 1730-1812, mar 1730-54 (with St Leonard Eastcheap), bur 1730-1812, **Ms 17609**. Rough bap 1795-8 and bur 1795-9, **in Ms 5672** (entries apparently identical to those in Ms 17609). Index to mar: **Boyd**.

Bap 1813-66 (with St Leonard Eastcheap), **in Ms 17610**. Rough bap 1813-47, **in Ms 5673** (entries apparently identical to those in Ms 17610). Rough bap 1850, **in Ms 5672**.

Mar 1754-1812, banns 1754-99 (both with St Leonard Eastcheap), **Ms 17611/1**. Index: **Boyd** (mar; also banns 1754-75).

Mar 1813-37 (with St Leonard Eastcheap), **Ms 17611/2**. Index: **Boyd**.

Mar 1837-65 (with St Leonard Eastcheap), **Ms 17611/3**.

Banns 1824-65 (with St Leonard Eastcheap), **Ms 5674**.

Bur 1813-53 (with St Leonard Eastcheap), **Ms 17612**. Rough bur 1813 (Jan.-Apr.), **in Ms 5675**. Rough bur 1813 (Apr.)-1849, **in Ms 5673** (some entries record, beside details in Ms 17612, causes of death). Index to Ms 17612: **in Webb 54/1-2**.

For later bap, mar and banns see Allhallows Lombard Street.

Transcripts:

Mar 1558-1837, banns 1754-99, **Challen 6**.

B tr of bap, mar and bur 1629-30/1, **in Ms 10107**; bap, mar and bur 1639-39/40, **in Ms 10107A**; bap, mar and bur 1801-2, 1804, 1807-9 and 1811-12, **Ms 10410**; bap 1813-32, 1836 and 1846-64, mar 1813-30 and 1836, bur 1813-32, 1836 and 1844-53 (all with St Leonard Eastcheap), **Ms 10452**.

ST BENET PAUL'S WHARF

United to St Nicholas Cole Abbey, 1879; the church has been used by a Welsh congregation since 1879

Partial index to bap and mar in **IGI**.

Receipts for bur (with names of deceased) 1605-56/7, in churchwardens' accounts, **in Ms 878/1**.

Bap 1619-1730, mar 1619-1715 (with St Peter Paul's Wharf from c.1680), bur 1619-1731/2, **Ms 5716**. Duplicate reg of bur 1678-1736, recording affidavits of bur in woollen, **Ms 5720/1**. Indexes: **Boyd** (mar); **in HS 38** (bap); **in HS 39** (mar); **in HS 41** (bur).

Bap 1730-1805, **Ms 5717/1**. Index: **in HS 38**.

Bap 1805-12, **Ms 5717/2**. Index: **in HS 38**.

Bap 1813-60, **Ms 5717/3**. Indexes: **in HS 38** (to 1837); **in Webb 3** (bap from 1838 of persons born before 1841).

Bap 1860-77, Welsh congregation bap 1880-1931, **Ms 5717/4**. Index: **in Webb 3** (bap of persons born before 1841).

Mar 1715-1879 (with St Peter Paul's Wharf, except 1828-34), entered in 8 vol as follows:

1715-28:	**Ms 5718/1**	1778-96:	**Ms 5729/2**
1728-42:	**Ms 5718/2**	1797-1812:	**Ms 5729/3**
1742/3-54:	**Ms 5718/3**	1813-37:	**Ms 5719/1**
1754-78:	**Ms 5729/1**	1837-79:	**Ms 5719/2**.

Indexes: **Boyd** (to 1837); **in HS 39** (to 1730/1); **in HS 40** (1731-1837).

Banns 1754-91 (with St Peter Paul's Wharf), **Ms 5730/1**.

Banns 1791-1879 (with St Peter Paul's Wharf), also Welsh congregation banns 1954-79, **Ms 5730/2**.

For banns 1879-89 (with St Peter Paul's Wharf), see St Nicholas Cole Abbey.

Bur 1731/2-1805, **Ms 5720/2**. Duplicate reg of bur to 1736, recording affidavits of bur in woollen, **Ms 5720/1**. Index: **in HS 41**.

Bur 1806-12, **Ms 5720/3**. Index: **in HS 41**.

Bur 1813-53, **Ms 5720/4**. Indexes: **in HS 41** (to 1837); **in Webb 3** (1837-53); **in Webb 54/1-2**.

Later reg (of Welsh congregation) retained by incumbent. For bap and mar of St Benet's parish from 1879, see St Nicholas Cole Abbey.

Transcripts:

Bap 1619-1837, **HS 38**. Indexed.

Mar 1619-1730/1, **HS 39**. Indexed

Mar 1731-1837, **HS 40**. Indexed.

Bur 1619-1837, **HS 41**. Indexed.

Bur 1837-53, **Webb 3**. Indexed.

B tr of bap, mar and bur 1800-12, **Ms 10421**; bap 1813-51, 1853-65 and 1867-8, mar 1813-37, bur 1813-51, **Ms 10421A**.

ST BENET SHEREHOG

United to St Stephen Walbrook, 1670

B tr of bap, mar and bur 1629-29/30, **in Ms 10107**; 1639-39/40, **in Ms 10107A**. Tr and index: **Webb 4**.

For reg from c.1670 see St Stephen Walbrook.

ST BOTOLPH ALDERSGATE (also known as ST BOTOLPH WITHOUT ALDERSGATE)

Partial index to bap and mar in **IGI**.

Receipts for bur (with names of deceased) 1468-16th century, in churchwardens' accounts, **in Ms 1454**, 105 rolls (list available at Mss enquiry desk). These rolls cover the period 1466-1636, but with many gaps. Full details of bur receipts are omitted from a number of the surviving rolls (none of the 17th century rolls include names of deceased).

Receipts for bur (with names of deceased) 1639-40, in churchwardens' accounts, **in Ms 1455/1**.

Bap 1638-1761, mar 1640-1754, banns 1653-64, bur 1640-1761, **Ms 3854**, 5 vol.

1. bap 1638-81, mar 1640-82, banns 1653-64, bur 1640-81
2. bap 1681/2-1707, mar 1682-1707, bur 1681/2-1707
3. bap, mar and bur 1707-18/9
4. bap, mar and bur 1718/9-25
5. bap 1725-61, mar 1725-54, bur 1725-61.

Indexes: **Boyd** (mar and banns); **in Ms 3860** (bap, surnames A-L); **in Ms 3861** (bap, surnames M-T, and mar, males only); **in Ms 3862/1** (bur, surnames A-G); **in Ms 3862/2** (bur, surnames H-S).

Bap and bur 1762-89, **Ms 3855**. Indexes: **in Ms 3860** (bap, surnames A-L); **in Ms 3861** (bap, surnames M-T); **in Ms 3862/1** (bur, surnames A-G); **in Ms 3862/2** (bur, surnames H-S).

Bap 1790-1984, **Ms 3856**, 4 vol. Index: in vol 1 (1790-1812).

1. 1790-1812 2. 1813-29 3. 1830-44 4. 1845-1984.

Mar 1754-1953, **Ms 3857**, 10 vol.

1. 1754-89
2. 1790-1812
3. 1813-29
4. 1830-37
5. 1837-46
6. 1846-57
7. 1857-72
8. 1872-1926
9. 1926-32
10. 1932-53.

Indexes: **Boyd** (to 1755); **in Ms 3861** (to 1789, males only); in vol 2 (1790-1812).

Banns 1779-1935, **Ms 3859,** 5 vol.
1. 1779-97
2. 1797-1821
3. 1821-38
4. 1838-57
5. 1857-1935.

Mar licences collection 1834-63, **Ms 11977/1**. Index: **in Ms 24657** (to 1838).

Mar licences collection 1864-1918, **Ms 11977/2**.

Bur 1790-1853, **Ms 3858**, 4 vol.
1. 1790-1812
2. 1813-28
3. 1829-47
4. 1848-53.

Index (1813-53): in J. Hanson and M. Stevens, *City of London burial index 1813-1853 part 3* (Milton Keynes, 1997?), fiches 104, **GL Printed Books Section**.

Transcripts:

Mar 1640-1755, banns 1653-64, **Challen 5**.

B tr of bap, mar and bur 1801, 1807-9 and 1811-47, **Ms 11335**, 5 boxes.
1. 1801, 1807-9 and 1811-15
2. 1816-23
3. 1824-30
4. 1831-7
5. 1838-47.

ST BOTOLPH ALDGATE (also known as ST BOTOLPH WITHOUT ALDGATE)

Partial index to bap in **IGI**.

Bap and mar 1558-1625, **Ms 9220**. Entries to 1599 in this reg are parchment copies. Original paper reg survive for 1571-93, **in Ms 9221**, and 1593-9, **in Ms 9223**. For banns, and for more detailed entries of bap and mar, 1583-1600 (incomplete), see parish clerks' memoranda books, **Ms 9234**, 7 vol, listed below. Index to reg: **in Ms 9233** (from 1593).

> Note: Ms 9223 alsocontains duplicate bap 1599-1607 and 1614-16 and mar 1599-1605 and 1614-16, copied from Ms 9220. Duplicate bap and mar 1616/7-25 are entered **in Ms 9234/8**.

Receipts for bur (with names of deceased) 1547-85, in churchwardens' accounts, **in Ms 9235/1**.

Bur 1558-1625 (Jul. 28), **Ms 9222/1**. Entries to 1599 in this reg are parchment copies. Original paper reg survive for 1571-93, **in Ms 9221**, and 1593-9, **in Ms 9223**. For more detailed entries of bur 1583-1600 (incomplete), see parish clerks' memoranda books, **Ms 9234,** 7 vol, listed below. Index to reg: **in Ms 9233** (from 1593).

> Note: Ms 9223 also contains duplicate bur 1599-1602 and 1614-16, copied from Ms 9222/1. Bur 1616/7-25 are also entered **in Ms 9234/8** (some entries record details not found in Ms 9222/1).

Parish clerks' memoranda books, including many rough bap, mar, banns and bur 1583-1600 and 1616/7-25, **Ms 9234**, 8 vol (recording more detail than the reg listed above).

1. 1583-4 and 1586-8
2. 1588-90 and 1591-2
3. 1590-l
4. 1593-4
5. 1594-6 and 1598-1600
6. 1596-7
7. 1597-8
8. 1616/7-25.

Bur 1625 (Jul. 28-31), not entered in any surviving reg, but included in the index, **Ms 9233**.

Bur 1625 (Aug.)-1665, **Ms 9222/2**. Duplicate bur 1653 (Oct.)-1654 (Jul.), **in Ms 9229**. Index: **in Ms 9233** (to 1640).

Bap 1625-69, mar 1625-56, bur 1665-73, **Ms 9224**. Rough bap 1625-40, **Ms 9225/1** (entries apparently identical to those in Ms 9224). Duplicate bap 1653 (Oct.)-1654 (Jul.), **in Ms 9229**. Index: **in Ms 9233** (to 1640).

Bap 1669-95 and 1711-18, **Ms 9225/2**.

Mar and banns 1653-8, mar 1658-75, **in Ms 9229**.

Mar 1675-95 and 1711-22, **Ms 9230/1**.

Bur 1673-95 and 1711-30, **Ms 9232/1**.

Bap, mar and bur 1695-1711, **Ms 9226**.

Bap 1711-18, **in Ms 9225/2**.

Bap 1718-52, **Ms 9225/3**. Rough bap 1735-49, **in Ms 9227** (recording, besides details in Ms 9225/3, whether parents were paupers).

Bap 1753-97, **Ms 9225/4**.

Bap 1797-1812, **Ms 9225/5**.

Bap 1813-15, **Ms 9231/1**.

Bap 1815-22, **Ms 9231/2**. Rough bap 1815-19, **Ms 9947** (entries apparently identical to those in Ms 9231/2).

Bap 1822-9, **Ms 9231/3**.

Bap 1829-35, **Ms 9231/4**.

Bap 1835-45, **Ms 9231/5**.

Bap 1845-56, **Ms 9231/6**.

Bap 1856-75, **Ms 9231/7**.

Bap 1876-1927 (with Holy Trinity Minories from 1897), **Ms 9231/8**.

Mar 1675-95 and 1711-1945 (with Holy Trinity Minories from 1898), **Ms 9230**, 20 vol. Males indexed 1795-1812 and 1822-31 (in vol 6 and 7).

1. 1675-95 and 1711-22	8. 1813-15	15. 1862-29
2. 1722-54	9. 1815-22	16. 1869-77
3. 1754-67	10. 1831-37	17. 1877-86
4. 1767-79	11. 1837-43	18. 1886-1915
5. 1779-95	12. 1843-48	19. 1916-33
6. 1795-1809	13. 1848-55	20. 1934-45
7. 1809-12 and 1822-31	14. 1855-62	

Note: for mar 1695-1711 see **Ms 9226** above.

Banns 1754-1846 and 1849-78, **Ms 9944**, 11 vol.

1. 1754-9	4. 1772-81	7. 1805-22	10. 1849-62
2. 1759-64	5. 1781-91	8. 1822-37	11. 1862-78.
3. 1764-72	6. 1791-1805	9. 1837-46	

Note: for banns 1846-9 see **Ms 9945/3** below.

Rough banns 1818-24 and 1832-49, **Ms 9945**, 3 vol.

1. 1818-24	2. 1832-8	3. 1839-49.

Bur 1711-30, **in Ms 9232/1**.

Bur 1730-67, **Ms 9232/2**. Rough bur 1745-49/50, **in Ms 9227** (recording fees paid).

Bur 1767-1812, **Ms 9232/3**.

Bur 1813-16, **Ms 9232/4**. Index: in J. Hanson and M. Stevens, *City of London burial index 1813-1853 part 3* (Milton Keynes, 1997?), fiches 104, **GL Printed Books Section**.

Bur 1816-36, **Ms 9232/5**. Index: in Hanson and Stevens, as above, **GL Printed Books Section**.

Bur 1836-53, **Ms 9232/6**. Index: in Hanson and Stevens, as above, **GL Printed Books Section**.

Later bap and mar reg retained by incumbent.

Transcripts:

B tr of bap 1802-3, mar 1802-9, bur 1802-3, **Ms 10422**; bap 1803-13, mar 1809-13, bur 1803-13, **Ms 11341**; bap, mar and bur 1814, **Ms 9232A/1**; mar 1815, **Ms 9232A/2**.

Index to bap, mar and bur 1593-1640, **Ms 9233**. The folio numbers in this index refer to a sequence of paper reg, of which 'Liber A' is Ms 9223, 'Liber C' is Ms 9234/8 and 'Liber D' is Ms 9225/1. Libri B, E and F do not appear to have survived, but the dates given in this index for entries in these missing vol can be used for reference to other reg covering the same period.

ST BOTOLPH BILLINGSGATE

United to St George Botolph Lane, 1670; St Mary at Hill, 1901

Partial index to bap in **IGI**.

Receipts for bur (with names of deceased), in churchwardens' accounts 1603-72, **in Ms 942/1**; 1678-1739, **in Ms 942/2**.

B tr of bap, mar and bur 1629-30/1, **in Ms 10107**; 1639-39/40, **in Ms 10107A**. Index: **in Webb 2**.

Bap 1685-1812, bur 1685/6-1812, **in Ms 4797**. Rough bap 1685-1727 and bur 1685-1726, **in Ms 4794** (with some variant entries). Index to Ms 4797: **in Webb 2**.

Bap 1813-91, **Ms 4801**. Duplicate bap 1813-29, **in Ms 4804**. Index: **in Webb 2** (to 1840).

Later bap entered in reg of St Mary at Hill.

Mar 1685/6-1812: see St George Botolph Lane.

Mar 1813-35, **Ms 4802**. Index: **in Webb 2**.

For later mar, and for banns from 1754 and mar licences from 1818, see St George Botolph Lane.

Bur 1813-45, **Ms 4803**. Duplicate bur 1813-30, **in Ms 4805**. Index: **in Webb 2 and 54/1-2** (to 1845).

Transcripts:

Bap, mar and bur 1629-30/1 and 1639-39/40 (from b tr), bap 1685-1840, bap 1841-91 of persons born before 1841, mar 1813-35, bur 1685/6-1845, **Webb 2**. Indexed.

Mar 1813-35, **Challen 41**.

B tr of bap, mar and bur 1629-30/1, **in Ms 10107**; 1639-39/40, **in Ms 10107A**; 1801-6 (mar from reg of St George Botolph Lane with St Botolph Billingsgate), **Ms 10424**. For later b tr see St George Botolph Lane.

ST BOTOLPH BISHOPSGATE (also known as ST BOTOLPH WITHOUT BISHOPSGATE)

Partial index to bap and mar in **IGI**.

Bap, mar and bur 1558-1628, **Ms 4515/1**. Indexes: **Boyd** (mar); in A.W.C. Hallen, *The registers of St Botolph Bishopsgate* (privately printed; Edinburgh, 1889-95), vol 1, **GL Printed Books Section**.

Bap 1628-57/8, mar 1629-77, banns 1653-60, bur 1628/9-57/8, entered in two vol, **Ms 4515/2-3**, as follows:

Bap 1628-53, mar 1629-53, bur 1628/9-53, **in Ms 4515/2**.
Bap and bur 1653-57/8, **in Ms 4515/3**.
Mar and banns 1653-60, **in Ms 4515/2 and Ms 4515/3** (registrations entered apparently at random in one or other of these vol).
Mar 1661-77, **in Ms 4515/2**.

Indexes: **Boyd** (mar and banns); in Hallen, as above, vol 1 (mar and banns), vol 2 (bur) and vol 3 (bap), **GL Printed Books Section**.

Bap 1658-77, mar 1677/8-1734, bur 1658-77, **Ms 4515/4**. Indexes: **Boyd** (mar); in Hallen, as above, vol 1 (mar), vol 2 (bur) and vol 3 (bap), **GL Printed Books Section**.

Bap 1677/8-1701, bur 1677/8-98, **Ms 4516/1**. Bur accounts from 1692, **in Ms 4534** (recording places of interment but omitting ages of deceased). Index to Ms 4516/1: in Hallen, as above, vol 2 (bur) and vol 3 (bap to 1690), **GL Printed Books Section**.

Bap 1701-17, bur 1698-1717, **Ms 4516/2**. Bur accounts to 1717, **in Ms 4534** (recording places of interment but omitting ages of deceased). Index to bur in Ms 4516/2: in Hallen, as above, vol 2, **GL Printed Books Section**.

Bap 1717-52, mar 1734-51, bur 1717-52, **Ms 4517/1**. Indexes to mar and bur: **Boyd** (mar); in Hallen, as above, vol 1 (mar) and vol 2 (bur), **GL Printed Books Section**.

Bap 1753-79, mar 1752-4, bur 1753-79, **Ms 4517/2**. Indexes to mar: **Boyd**; in Hallen, as above, vol 1, **GL Printed Books Section**.

Bap and bur 1780-1802, **Ms 4518/1**.

Bap and bur 1803-12, **Ms 4518/2**.

Bap 1813-98, **Ms 4519**, 8 vol. Indexed 1836-98 (in vol 4-8).

1. 1813-20	3. 1828-35	5. 1843-50	7. 1859-69
2. 1820-28	4. 1836-43	6. 1850-59	8. 1870-98.

Mar 1754-1958, **Ms 4520**, 27 vol. Indexed, males only, 1754-1837 (in vol 1-12).

1. 1754-67	8. 1808-12	15. 1846-50	22. 1876-84
2. 1768-74	9. 1813-18	16. 1850-53	23. 1884-1901
3. 1774-84	10. 1818-24	17. 1853-57	24. 1901-15
4. 1784-89	11. 1825-32	18. 1857-61	25. 1915-26
5. 1790-03	12. 1833-37	19. 1861-65	26. 1927-44
6. 1793-1802	13. 1837-40	20. 1865-71	27. 1944-58.
7. 1802-08	14. 1840-46	21. 1871-76	

Banns 1833-8, **Ms 4522/1**.

Banns 1838-47, **Ms 21138**.

Banns 1847-54, **Ms 4522/2**.

Banns 1854-61, **Ms 4522/3**.

Banns 1861-9, **Ms 4522/4**.

Banns 1869-1925, **Ms 4522/5**.

Banns 1925-50, **Ms 4522/6**.

Mar licences collection 1848-73, **Ms 21327**, 3 vol.

1. 1848-54 2. 1855-62 3. 1863-73.

Index: **Ms 21328**.

Rough bur 1792-1800, **Ms 21135**, 2 vol (recording dates and causes of death, places of interment and fees paid).

1. 1792-95 2. 1796-1800.

Bur accounts 1792-1802, **Ms 21136** (recording places of interment and fees paid).

Bur 1813-21, **Ms 4521/1**. Index: in J. Hanson and M. Stevens, *City of London burial index 1813-1853 part 3* (Milton Keynes, 1997?), fiches 104, **GL Printed Books Section**.

Bur 1822-31, **Ms 4521/2**. Bur accounts 1830-1, **in Ms 21137** (recording places of interment and fees paid). Index to Ms 4521/2: in Hanson and Stevens, as above, **GL Printed Books Section**.

Bur 1831-41, **Ms 4521/3**. Bur accounts 1831-41, **in Ms 21137** (recording places of interment and fees paid). Index to Ms 4521/3: in Hanson and Stevens, as above, **GL Printed Books Section**.

Bur 1841-9 (Sep.), **in Ms 4521/4**. Indexed. Bur accounts 1841-9, in **Ms 21137** (recording places of interment and fees paid), also 1849 (Jan.-Aug.), **in Ms 4521A** (recording places of interment). Ms 4521/4 also indexed in Hanson and Stevens, as above, **GL Printed Books Section**.

Funeral accounts 1851-67, **in Ms 4521A** (recording fees paid for funeral services held in the church after closure of the churchyard). Three bur 1853-5, **in Ms 4521/4**.

Later bap and mar reg retained by incumbent.

Transcripts:

Bap 1558-1628, mar 1558-1754, bur 1558-1628/9, Hallen, as above, vol 1, **GL Printed Books Section**. Indexed.

Bap 1628-90, Hallen, as above, vol 3, **GL Printed Books Section**. Indexed.

Bur 1628/9-1752, Hallen, as above, vol 2, **GL Printed Books Section**. Indexed.

B tr of bap, mar and bur 1639-40, **in Ms 10107A**; bap 1800-62, mar 1800-37, bur 1800-53, **Ms 11336**, 9 boxes (list available at Mss enquiry desk).

ST BRIDE FLEET STREET

Partial index to bap and mar in **IGI**.

List of 'presumed bur' (i.e. of wills in which the testator wished to be buried at St Bride Fleet Street) 1274-1587, **in Ms 6539**.

Bap 1587-87/8, bur 1587-95, **Ms 6535**.

Bap 1587/8-1653, **Ms 6536**.

Mar 1587-1653, **Ms 6537**.

Bur 1595-1653, **Ms 6538**.

Bap 1653-72 (Sep.) and 1673 (Dec.)-1674 (Apr.), mar 1653-66, bur 1653-72 (Jun.), **Ms 6540/1**. Bur accounts 1665-65/6 and 1670-2 (Apr.), **Ms 6570/1** (incomplete; recording some addresses).

Bap 1672 (Sep.)-1673 (Jul.), mar 1666-75, bur 1672 (Jul.)-1673 (Nov.): no reg for these dates are known to exist.

Bap 1673 (Aug.)-1695, mar 1675/6-95, bur 1673 (Dec.)-1695, **Ms 6540/2**. Duplicate bap 1673 (Dec.)-1674 (Apr.), **in Ms 6540/1**. Bur accounts 1677-82/3, **in Ms 6570/3** (incomplete). Bap accounts 1685/6-89 and 1691/2-94/5 and bur accounts 1685-94/5, **in Ms 6620**. Rough bap accounts 1693 (Jun.) (recording addresses) and rough bur accounts 1686 (Oct.-Nov.) and 1689/90 (Jan.) (recording addresses and causes of death), **in Ms 6620A**. Rough mar and bur from 1695, **in Ms 6548** (containing much biographical detail not found in Ms 6540/2).

Bap, mar and bur 1695-1714, **Ms 6540/3**. Rough bap, mar and bur 1695-1706, **Ms 6548** (containing much biographical detail not found in Ms 6540/3). Bap and bur accounts 1698-9, **in Ms 6620**. Rough bur from 1709, **in Ms 6550** (recording, besides details in Ms 6540/3, addresses and causes of death).

Bap, mar and bur 1714-36, **Ms 6540/4**. Rough bur to 1726/7 (Jan.), **in Ms 6550** (recording, besides details in Ms 654014, addresses and causes of death).

Bap 1736-1812, **Ms 6541/1**. Rough bap from 1800, **in Ms 6563** (entries apparently identical to those in Ms 6541/1).

Bap 1813-29, **Ms 6541/2**. Rough bap to 1815, **in Ms 6563**, and from 1815, **in Ms 6549/1** (both recording complete addresses for some entries where Ms 6541/2 gives less detail).

Bap 1830-44, **Ms 6541/3**. Rough bap 1830 (Jan.-Apr.), **in Ms 6549/1**, and 1830 (May)-1832, **Ms 6549/2** (entries apparently identical to those in Ms 6541/3).

Bap 1844-59, **Ms 6541/4**.

Bap 1859-1939 and 1952 (one entry only) (with Bridewell chapelry from 1864 and with Holy Trinity Gough Square from 1906), **Ms 6541/5**.

Mar 1736-1969 (with Bridewell chapelry from 1864 and with Holy Trinity Gough Square from 1906), **Ms 6542**, 27 vol.

1. 1736-75	8. 1826-29	15. 1848-51	22. 1904-34
2. 1775-94	9. 1830-34	16. 1851-55	23. 1934-53
3. 1794-1810	10. 1834-37	17. 1855-59	24. 1953-58
4. 1810-12	11. 1837-39	18. 1859-65	25. 1958-61
5. 1813-17	12. 1839-42	19. 1865-70	26. 1961-56
6. 1817-21	13. 1842-45	20. 1870-80	27. 1966-59.
7. 1822-26	14. 1845-48	21. 1880-1904	

Banns 1735-1825 and 1850-1908 (with Bridewell chapelry from 1864 and with Holy Trinity Gough Square from 1906), **Ms 6544**, 9 vol.

1. 1735-54	4. 1776-89	7. 1813-25
2. 1754-67	5. 1789-1802	8. 1850-81
3. 1767-76	6. 1802-13	9. 1881-1908.

Mar licences collection 1869-72 and 1883-1907 (with Bridewell chapelry), **Ms 6621**, 4 boxes.

1. 1869-72	2. 1883-91	3. 1892-97	4. 1898-1907.

Bur 1736-1812, **Ms 6543/1**. Bur accounts 1742-42/3 and 1743-45/6, **in Ms 6570/3** (incomplete); 1743 (Apr.) and 1745/6 (Feb.-Mar.), **in Ms 6570/1**.

Bur 1813-29, **Ms 6543/2**. Rough bur 1820-9, **Ms 6551/1** (recording, besides details in Ms 6543/2, places of interment and causes of death). Index to Ms 6543/2: in J. Hanson and M. Stevens, *City of London burial index 1813-1853 part 3* (Milton Keynes, 1997?), fiches 104, **GL Printed Books Section**.

Bur 1830-46, **Ms 6543/3**. Rough bur 1830-8, **Ms 6551/2**, and from 1838, **in Ms 6551/3** (both recording, besides details in Ms 6543/3, places of interment and causes of death). Index to Ms 6543/3: in Hanson and Stevens, as above, **GL Printed Books Section**.

Bur 1846-54, **Ms 6543/4**. Rough bur for these dates, **in Ms 6551/3** (recording, besides details in Ms 6543/4, places of interment and causes of death). Index to Ms 6543/4: in Hanson and Stevens, as above, **GL Printed Books Section**.

For bap 1842-1906, mar 1869-1906 and banns 1879-1906, see also Holy Trinity Gough Square.

Later bap and mar reg retained by incumbent.

Transcripts:

Bap 1587-1626, **Ms 6545/1**. Bap 1626-53, **Ms 6545/2**. Mar 1587-1653, **Ms 6546**. Bur 1587-95, **in Ms 6539**. Bur 1595-1618, **Ms 6547/1**. Bur 1618-37, **Ms 6547/2**. Bur 1637-53, **Ms 6547/3**.

B tr of bap 1801-72 and 1874, mar 1801-38, bur 1801-54, **Ms 11439**, 7 boxes.

1. 1801-9	3. 1817-22	5. 1831-6	7. 1847-72 and 1874
2. 1810-16	4. 1823-30	6. 1837-46	

ST CHRISTOPHER LE STOCKS

United to St Margaret Lothbury, 1781

Partial index to bap and mar in **IGI**.

Bap, mar and bur 1557-1653, **in Ms 4421/1**. Index: **Boyd** (mar).

Bap 1653-1781, births of unbaptised children 1696/7-1704, mar 1653-1754, bur 1653-1781, **Ms 4421/2**. One bap 1654 (Apr.) and five mar 1654-6, **in Ms 4421/1**. Index: **Boyd** (mar).

Mar 1754-80, banns 1755-80, **Ms 4422**. Index: **Boyd**.

Mar licences collection 1775-9, **Ms 24136**. Index: **in Ms 24657**.

For later reg and for mar licences collection from 1781 see St Margaret Lothbury.

Transcripts:

Bap 1557-1781, births of unbaptised children 1696/7-1704, mar 1557-1780, banns 1755-80, bur 1557-1781, E. Freshfield, *The register book of the parish of St Christopher le Stocks* (London, 1882), **GL Printed Books Section**.

B tr of bap, mar and bur 1664-65/6, **in Ms 10952**.

ST CLEMENT EASTCHEAP

Partial index to bap and mar in **IGI**.

Bap 1539-1812, mar 1539-1754 (with St Martin Orgar from 1688), bur 1539-1812, **Ms 4783**. Indexes: **Boyd** (mar); **in HS 67-8** (bap, mar and bur).

Mar 1754-86 (with St Martin Orgar), **Ms 4785/1**. Indexes: **Boyd**; **in HS 67**.

Mar 1787-1812, banns 1787-1830 (both with St Martin Orgar), **Ms 4785/2**. Indexes: **Boyd** (mar; also banns 1801-30); **in HS 67** (mar).

Bap 1813-1940, mar 1813-37 (May), bur 1813-53 (all with St Martin Orgar), **Ms 4786**. Includes duplicate mar to 1839, also entered in Ms 29734. Indexes: **Boyd** (mar); **in HS 67-8** (bap to 1839, mar and bur); **in Webb 3** (bap 1840-1940 of persons born before 1841); **in Webb 54/1-2** (bur).

Later bap reg retained by incumbent.

Mar 1837 (Jul.)-1964 (with St Martin Orgar), **Ms 29734**. Duplicate mar to 1839 also entered in Ms 4786.

Banns 1831-1928 (with St Martin Orgar), **Ms 20490**.

Transcripts:

Bap and mar 1539-1839, bur 1539-1853, **HS 67-8**. Indexed.

Mar 1539-1839, banns 1787-1830, **Challen 6**.

B tr of bap 1801-34 and 1837-50 (with St Martin Orgar from 1809), mar 1801-34, 1837-8 and 1841-50 (with St Martin Orgar), bur 1801-34 and 1837-50 (with St Martin Orgar from 1809), **Ms 11177**.

ST DIONIS BACKCHURCH

United to Allhallows Lombard Street, 1876; St Edmund the King and Martyr, 1937

Partial index to bap and mar in **IGI**.

Bap 1538-1666 and 1668-1736/7, mar 1538-1666 and 1674-1736, bur 1538-1736/7, **Ms 17602**. Bur accounts 1706, **Ms 18483A**. Indexes to Ms 17602: **Boyd** (mar); **in HS 3** (bap, mar and bur).

Bap 1737-1812, mar 1737-54, bur 1737-1812, **Ms 17603**. Indexes: **Boyd** (mar); **in HS 3** (bap, mar and bur to 1754).

Bap 1813-56, **Ms 17604/1**.

Bap 1857-77, **Ms 17604/2**.

Mar 1754-1877, **Ms 17605**, 4 vol. Index: **Boyd** (to 1837).
1. 1754-1812 2. 1813-37 (Feb.) 3. 1837 (Apr.) 4. 1837 (Jul.)-77.

Mar accounts 1829-42, **in Ms 18483**.

Banns 1754-1823, **Ms 11256/1**. Index: **Boyd** (except 1776-1800).

Banns 1823-77, **Ms 11256/2**.

Bur 1813-49, **Ms 17606**. Bur accounts 1829-42, **in Ms 18483**. Index to Ms 17606: **in Webb 54/1-2**.

For later bap, mar and banns see Allhallows Lombard Street.

Transcripts:

Bap, mar and bur 1538-1754, **HS 3**. Indexed.

Mar 1754-1837, banns 1754-1823, **Challen 6**.

B tr of bap, mar and bur 1814-37, **Ms 10455**; bap 1838-56, bur 1838-45 and 1847-9, **Ms 10455A**. Note: b tr of bap, mar and bur 1799-1802 and 1813 are held by Lambeth Palace Library, London SE1 7JU.

ST DUNSTAN IN THE EAST

United to Allhallows Barking by the Tower, 1960

Partial index to bap and mar in **IGI**.

Receipts for bur (with names of deceased) 1495-1506, in churchwardens' accounts, **in Ms 4887**. Transcribed **in Ms 4888**.

Bap, mar and bur 1558-1653, **Ms 7857/1**. Note: bap 1598 (Nov.)-1599 (May), mar 1593 (Oct.)-1605/6 (Jan.) and bur 1597/8 (Mar.)-1605 (Dec.) missing; bap 1599 (May)-1605 (Dec.), also some additional bap 1589-98, 1608/9 and 1646/7-52/3, entered out of sequence. Indexes: **Boyd** (mar 1605/6-25); **in HS 69** (bap, mar and bur).

Bap, mar and bur 1653-76, **Ms 7857/2**. Index: **in HS 84-5**.

Bap 1676-1766, mar 1676-1754, bur 1676-1766, **Ms 7857/3**. Indexes: **in HS 84-7** (bap to 1758, mar to 1754, bur to 1766); **in Ms 8023/1** (bap 1700-66); **Ms 8025/1** (bur 1700-66).

Bap 1766-1812, **Ms 7858/1**. Rough bap 1783-1809, **in Ms 5069** (entries apparently identical to those in Ms 7858/1). Index 1766-1812: in reg.

Note: There is also an index of bap to 1782, **in Ms 8023/1**, giving page numbers which refer, not to Ms 7858/1, but to a duplicate reg (probably containing bap 1766-82) damaged beyond repair by enemy action in 1941 and not available for use.

Bap 1813-1938 (**Ms 31358**) damaged beyond repair by enemy action in 1941 and not available for use: use instead the full transcript, compiled 1997 by Guildhall Library staff, **Ms 31359A** on Reading Room shelves, or the duplicate copy, **Ms 31359**. Duplicate bap 1813-16, **in Ms 7858/2**. Index 1813-61 (compiled before reg was damaged): **Ms 8023/2** (does not give dates of bap, but refers to numbered entries 1-1107 in the damaged reg; for instructions as to use of index, see explanatory note at front of vol).

Bap 1948, **in Ms 7858/2**.

Mar 1754-99, **Ms 7859/1**. Index (of males): **in Ms 8024**.

Mar 1799-1812, **Ms 7859/2**. Index (of males): in reg.

Mar 1813-16, **Ms 8026**. Tr **in Ms 7859/3**. Indexes (of males): **in Ms 8026A**; **in Ms 8024**.

Mar 1816-37, **Ms 7859/3**. Includes tr of mar 1813-16, from Ms 8026. Indexes (of males): **Ms 8026A**; **in Ms 8024**.

Mar 1837-1939, **Ms 7859/4**.

Banns 1754-89, **Ms 8028**.

Banns 1821-51, **Ms 4884**.

Bur 1766-1812, **Ms 7860/1**. Rough bur 1783, **in Ms 5069** (recording places of interment in greater detail than Ms 7860/1), and 1792-1826, **Ms 4885** (recording ages of deceased; some entries also record places of interment in greater detail than Ms 7860/1). Index 1766-1812: in reg.

Bur 1813-14, **Ms 8027**. Tr **in Ms 7860/2**. Rough bur for these dates, **in Ms 4885** (recording additional details not found in Ms 8027). Indexes to Ms 8027: **in Ms 8025/2**; **in Webb 54/1-2**.

Bur 1814-53, **Ms 7860/2**. Includes tr of bur 1813-14, from Ms 8027. Rough bur to 1826, **in Ms 4885** (recording additional details not found in Ms 7860/2). Indexes to Ms 7860/2: **Ms 8025/2**; **in Webb 54/1-2**.

Transcripts:

Bap, mar and bur 1558-1653, **HS 69**. Indexed.

Bap, mar and bur 1653-91/2, **HS 84-5**. Indexed.

Bap 1692-1758, mar 1692-1754, bur 1692-1766, **HS 86-7**. Indexed.

Mar 1605/6-25, J.L.V. Pruyn, in *The Genealogist*, N.S. vol 11 (1895), pp 36-47, **GL Printed Books Section**.

Bap 1813-1938, compiled 1997 by Guildhall Library staff, **Ms 31359A** on Reading Room shelves, also duplicate, **Ms 31359**.

Tr of extracts from bap 1818-20, 1841-4, 1859-66 and 1909-16, **in Ms 3713/1**.

B tr of bap 1815-16, 1846-52, 1854-6 and 1858-9, mar 1815-16, bur 1815-16 and 1846-52, **Ms 14562**. Note: b tr of bap, mar and bur 1799-1800, 1804, 1806-10, 1812-14 and 1837-8 are held by Lambeth Palace Library, London SE1 7JU.

ST DUNSTAN IN THE WEST

Partial index to bap and mar in **IGI**.

Receipts for bur (with names of deceased) 1516-1608, in churchwardens' accounts, **in Ms 2968/1**.

Bap 1558-1669/70, mar 1559/60-1658, banns 1653-55/6, bur 1558-1669: entered in two concurrent series, one parchment, the other paper. Ms 10343 is probably the original paper reg, of which Ms 10342 is the parchment copy; but the subsequent relationship of the two series is not known. The entries in each series are usually identical, but there are some gaps in the series of paper reg.

Parchment series:
Bap 1558-1631/2, mar 1559/60-1631/2, bur 1558-1631/2, **Ms 10342**.
Bap 1632-69/70, mar 1632-58, banns 1653-55/6, bur 1632-69, **Ms 10345**.

Paper series:
Bap 1599/1600-1622, mar 1559/60-1622, bur 1558-1614, **Ms 10343**.
Bap 1623-45, mar 1625-45, bur 1623-45, **Ms 10344** (bap 12-24 Aug. 1642 entered twice).
Bap 1645-57, mar 1645-53, bur 1645-56, **Ms 10346** (many mar entries 1648-50 missing).

Rough bap and bur 1642/3-45, **Ms 10357** (many entries not in chronological order).
Rough bap and bur 1650-3, **Ms 10358**. Both record some details not found in the other reg.

Bap 1669/70-1707, bur 1669-1709, **Ms 10348**.

Bap 1707-39, **Ms 10349**.

Bap 1739-71, **Ms 10351**.

Bap 1771-94, **Ms 10355/1**. Index: **Ms 10359/l** (1771-94 A-D and 1771-84 E-Z).

Bap 1795-1812, **Ms 10355/2**. Indexed.

Bap 1813-36, entered in four vol, **Ms 10355/3-6**, with duplication of entries, as follows:
Bap 1813 (Jan.)-1832 (Jul.), **Ms 10355/3**. Index: **Ms 10359/2**.
Bap 1813 (Jan.) and 1815 (Jan.)-1822 (Nov.), **Ms 10355/4**. Index: **Ms 10359/3**.
Bap 1822 (Nov.)-1836 (Oct.), **Ms 10355/5**. Index: **Ms 10359/4**.
Bap 1832 (Jun.)-1833 (Jun.), **Ms 10355/6**.

Each of these four vol is apparently complete for the period stated, and the duplicated entries, although sometimes in different hands, are identical.

Bap 1836-43, **Ms 10355/7**.

Bap 1844-57, **Ms 10355/8**.

Bap 1858-1990, **Ms 10355/9**.

Mar 1658-1739, banns 1655/6-59, **Ms 10347**. Index: **Boyd** (from 1701).

Mar 1739-54, **Ms 10352**. Index: **Boyd**.

Mar 1754-1970, **Ms 10354**, 22 vol.

1. 1754-62	7. 1837-48	13. 1904-15	19. 1954-9
2. 1762-79	8. 1848-54	14. 1915-28	20. 1959-64
3. 1779-96	9. 1855-60	15. 1928-36	21. 1964-9
4. 1796-1812	10. 1861-70	16. 1936-43	22. 1969-70.
5. 1813-26	11. 1870-81	17. 1943-7	
6. 1826-37	12. 1881-1903	18. 1947-53	

Indexes: **Boyd** (to 1775, and selectively c.1801-12); **Ms 10360/1** (1779-96, males); **Ms 10360/2** (1797-1812, males); **Ms 10360/3** (1813-26, males); **Ms 10360/4** (1826-37, males).

Banns 1754-7, **in Ms 10354/1**. Index: **Boyd**.

Banns 1811-41, **Ms 3072**.

Banns 1891-1959, **Ms 18519**.

Mar licences collection 1731-1884, **Ms 10354A**. Index: **in Ms 24657** (to 1838).

Bur 1709-39, **Ms 10350**.

Bur 1739-91, **Ms 10353**.

Bur 1791-1812, **Ms 10356/1**. Indexed.

Bur 1813-30, **Ms 10356/2**. Indexes: **Ms 10361/1**; in J. Hanson and M. Stevens, *City of London burial index 1813-1853 part 3* (Milton Keynes, 1997?), fiches 104, **GL Printed Books Section**.

Bur 1831-56, **Ms 10356/3**. Bur accounts 1838-49, **Ms 2970**. Indexes to Ms 10356/3: **Ms 10361/2** (giving dates of bur); **Ms 10361/3** (giving page numbers from reg); in Hanson and Stevens, as above, **GL Printed Books Section**.

Registrar's returns of deaths 1879-81 and 1884-6, **Ms 10361A**.

One bur 1927, **in Ms 10356/2**.

For bap 1842-86 and mar 1845-85, see also St Thomas in the Liberty of the Rolls.

Transcripts:

Bur 1845-50, **Ms 18518**.

B tr of bap, mar and bur 1639-39/40, **in Ms 10107A**; bap 1800-2, 1804-5, 1807-11, 1813 and 1820-1, **Ms 10111**; mar 1800-11, 1813 and 1820-1, **Ms 10112**; bur 1800-11, 1813 and 1820-1, **Ms 10113**; bap, mar and bur 1812, 1814-19 and 1822-4, **Ms 10114/1-10** (one box); bap, mar and bur 1825-37, **Ms 10114/11-23** (one box); bap and bur 1838-43, 1845-6 and 1848-9, **Ms 10113A**.

ST EDMUND THE KING AND MARTYR

Partial index to bap and mar in **IGI**.

Bap 1670-1789, mar 1673-1754 (with St Nicholas Acons), bur 1670-1789, **Ms 20204**. Indexes: **Boyd** (mar); in W. Brigg, *The Parish Registers of St Edmund the King and Martyr* (privately printed; London, 1892), **GL Printed Books Section** (bap, mar and bur).

Bap and bur 1789-1812, **Ms 20205**. Rough bap and bur from 1804, **in Ms 11440** (with some variant entries). Index to Ms 20205: in Brigg, as above, **GL Printed Books Section.**

Bap 1813-1980 (with St Nicholas Acons from 1875; also, from 1937, with Allhallows Lombard Street, St Benet Gracechurch, St Leonard Eastcheap and St Dionis Backchurch), **Ms 20206**. Rough bap 1804-20, **in Ms 11440**, and 1820-64, **in Ms 11441** (both with some variant entries). Index to bap 1813-40: **in Webb 1**.

Mar 1754-1802 (with St Nicholas Acons), **Ms 20207/1**. Indexes: **Boyd**; in Brigg, as above, **GL Printed Books Section**.

Mar 1802-12 (with St Nicholas Acons), **Ms 20207/2**. Indexes: **Boyd**; in Brigg, as above, **GL Printed Books Section**.

Mar 1813-37, **Ms 20208**. Index: **in Webb 1**.

Mar 1837-1982 (with St Nicholas Acons from 1851; also, from 1937, with Allhallows Lombard Street, St Benet Gracechurch, St Leonard Eastcheap and St Dionis Backchurch), **Ms 29090**.

Banns 1811-44 and 1881-2 (with St Nicholas Acons), **Ms 17625/1**.

Banns 1844-79 and 1882-1980 (with St Nicholas Acons; also, from 1937, with Allhallows Lombard Street, St Benet Gracechurch, St Leonard Eastcheap and St Dionis Backchurch), **Ms 17625/2**.

Bur 1813-50, **Ms 20210**. Rough bur 1804-20, **in Ms 11440**, and 1820-50, **in Ms 11442** (both with some variant entries). List of bur in chancel vaults 1805-50, **Ms 11442A**; in churchyard 1826-48, **Ms 20211**. Index to bur 1813-50: **in Webb 1 and 54/1-2**.

Transcripts:

Bap 1670-1812, mar 1673-1812, bur 1670-1789, Brigg, as above, **GL Printed Books Section**. Indexed.

Bap 1813-40, bap 1841-51 of persons born before 1841, mar 1813-37, bur 1813-50, **Webb 1**. Indexed. Note: compiled from b tr of bap, mar and bur (Mss 10453-3A) and from rough reg of bap and bur (Mss 11440-2), not from original reg.

B tr of bap, mar and bur 1800-3 and 1807-37, **Ms 10453**; bap 1838-45, 1847-9 and 1851-60, bur 1838-45 and 1847-50, **Ms 10453A**.

ST ETHELBURGA BISHOPSGATE

Partial index to bap and mar in **IGI**.

Receipts for bur (with names of deceased) 1569-1681, in churchwardens' accounts, **in Ms 4241/1**.

Bap 1671-1722, mar 1679-1723, bur 1672-1723, **Ms 4236/1**. Index: **Boyd** (mar). Bap 1723-92, mar 1723-54, bur 1723-92, **Ms 4236/2**. Index: **Boyd** (mar).

Bap and bur 1792-1812, **Ms 4238**.

Mar 1754-92, **Ms 4237** (in two sequences: mar by licence 1755-91 and, at back, mar by banns 1754-92). Indexes: in reg (incomplete); **in Webb 4**.

Mar 1792-1812, **Ms 4239** (in two sequences: mar by licence and, at back, mar by banns). Indexes: in reg (males only); **Boyd**.

Bap 1812-73, mar 1813-37, bur 1813-49, **Ms 4240**. Indexes: **Boyd** (mar); in J. Hanson and M. Stevens, *City of London burial index 1813-1853 part 3* (Milton Keynes, 1997?), fiches 104, **GL Printed Books Section** (bur).

Bap 1873-1974, **Ms 25118**.

Mar 1837-1986, **Ms 9361**, 5 vol.

1. 1837-1932	3. 1935-40	5. 1954-86.
2. 1932-5	4. 1940-51	

Banns 1809-23 and 1865-77, **Ms 9362/1**.

Banns 1878-1936, **Ms 9362/2**.

Banns 1936-53, **Ms 9362/3**.

Transcripts:

Bap 1671-1914, mar 1679-1754 and 1792-1915, bur 1672-1849, W. F. Cobb, *The registers of the church of St Ethelburga ... within Bishopsgate* (privately printed; London, 1915), **GL Printed Books Section**. Note: only names and years are transcribed; for exact dates of bap, mar and bur the original reg should be consulted.

Mar 1754-92, **Webb 4**. Indexed.

B tr of bap, mar and bur 1800-4, 1805 (May)-1806 (May) and 1807-12, **Ms 11174**; bap 1813-50, mar 1813-37, bur 1813-44, **Ms 11174A**.

ST EWIN

Amalgamated with St Nicholas Shambles to form Christchurch Newgate Street, 1547

No reg extant. See Christchurch Newgate Street.

ST FAITH UNDER ST PAUL

United to St Augustine Watling Street, 1670; St Mary le Bow, 1954

Partial index to bap in **IGI**.

Bap and bur 1645-85/6, **Ms 8882**. Bap 1668-80 and bur 1669/70-80/1 also **in Ms 8883** (some entries omitted; some others differ from those in Ms 8882). Reg of affidavits of bur in woollen 1678-80, **in Ms 8873**.

Bap 1685/6-1720/1, bur 1685/6-1723, **Ms 8884**. Includes tr of bap and bur 1680-85/6 from Ms 8882; also mar 1690-90/1 and 1695-8, duplicates of St Faith entries in the reg of St Augustine Watling Street with St Faith under St Paul (Ms 8872/2-3).

Bap 1720/1-68, bur 1723-1800, **Ms 8885**. Reg of affidavits of bur in woollen 1730-1, **in Ms 8873**.

Bap 1768-1812, **Ms 8886/1**. Three rough bap 1812, **in Ms 8894/2**.

Bap 1813-1900, **Ms 8886/2**. Rough bap 1813-23, **in Ms 8894/2** (some entries omitted; others apparently identical to those in Ms 8886/2).

Mar 1674-1812: see St Augustine Watling Street.

Mar 1813-37, **Ms 8887**. Indexed in **Boyd,** but incorrectly attributed therein to St Augustine Watling Street.

Bur 1801-12, **Ms 8888/1**. Rough bur from 1803, **in Ms 25742**.

Bur 1813-53, **Ms 8888/2**. Rough bur 1803-53, **in Ms 25742**. Index to Ms 8888/2: **in Webb 54/1-2**.

For later reg (bap from 1909, mar from 1837, banns from 1754) see St Augustine Watling Street.

Transcripts:

Mar 1813-37, **Challen 13**.

B tr of bap 1813-45 and 1847-52, mar 1813-36, bur 1813-52, **Ms 14563**.

ST GABRIEL FENCHURCH
United to St Margaret Pattens, 1670

Partial index to bap and mar in **IGI**.

Bap 1571-1709, mar 1572-1683/4, bur 1571-1709, **Ms 5293**. Index to mar: **in Webb 16 and 40**.

Bap and bur 1709-1812, **Ms 5294**.

Bap 1813-1901, **Ms 5295**.

Mar 1814-37, **Ms 5296**. Index: **in Webb 16 and 40**.

Bur 1813-51, **Ms 5297**. Index: **in Webb 54/1-2**.

For bap c.1901-52, mar c.1683/4-1812 and 1837-1952, banns 1754-1881, see St Margaret Pattens.

Transcripts:

Mar 1572-1683/4 and 1814-37, **Webb 16**. Index: **in Webb 16** (places) **and 40** (names).

B tr of bap and bur 1801, 1803-5 and 1807-12, **Ms 10458** (also containing b tr of mar 1801, 1804-5 and 1807-12, from reg of St Margaret Pattens with St Gabriel Fenchurch). For later b tr see St Margaret Pattens.

ST GEORGE BOTOLPH LANE

United to St Mary at Hill, 1901

Partial index to bap and mar in **IGI**.

Bap 1547/8-1617, mar 1547-1616/7, banns 1580-95, bur 1546-1616, **Ms 4791**. Parchment copy of bap 1547/8-1612, mar 1547-1610/1, bur 1546-1612, **Ms 4792** (most entries apparently identical to those in Ms 4791, but some entries c.1597-9 contain additional detail). Index to mar: **Boyd**.

Note: each of these two vol includes a selective list of bur 1390-1545/6, compiled in 1574 from monumental inscriptions in the church and churchyard. Ms 4791 also includes notes of places of interment in the church and chancel 1570-97; and one bap 1619 and seven bur 1616-17, duplicates of entries in Ms 4793.

Bap 1617-85, mar 1617-83, bur 1616-85, **Ms 4793**. Dates of birth 1653/4-59/60 and banns 1653/4-60, **in Ms 4794** (also contains duplicate bur entries 1653/4-59/60). Index to mar: **Boyd**.

Bap 1685-1812, mar 1685/6-1754 (with St Botolph Billingsgate), bur 1685-1812, **in Ms 4795**. Rough bap 1685-1725/6, mar 1685/6-1720 and bur 1685-1726, **in Ms 4794** (with some variant bap and bur entries; mar entries in abbreviated form). Index to mar: **Boyd**.

Bap 1813-91, **Ms 4798**. Duplicate bap 1813-30, **in Ms 4804**.

Mar 1754-1812, banns 1754-1842 (both with St Botolph Billingsgate), **Ms 4796**. Duplicate mar 1754-79, **in Ms 4795**. Index to mar: **Boyd**.

Mar 1813-37, **Ms 4799**. Index: **Boyd**.

Mar 1837-90 (with St Botolph Billingsgate), **Ms 4552**.

Mar licences collection 1818-88 (with St Botolph Billingsgate), **Ms 955**. Index: **in Ms 24657** (to 1838).

Bur 1813-48, **Ms 4800**. Duplicate bur 1813-30, **in Ms 4805**. Index to Ms 4800: **in Webb 54/1-2**.

Later bap, mar and banns entered in reg of St Mary at Hill (mar reg retained by incumbent).

Transcripts:

Mar 1547-1837, **Challen 41**.

Mar 1780-1812, **in Ms 4797**.

B tr of bap, mar and bur 1801-6, **Ms 11169**; 1807-9 and 1812-53 (all with St Botolph Billingsgate), **Ms 11236**. Note: bur 1849-53 are nil returns.

ST GILES CRIPPLEGATE

Partial index to bap and mar in **IGI**.

Bap, mar and bur 1561-88, **Ms 6418** (original paper reg). Parchment copy for these dates in **Ms 6419/1**.

Bap 1561-1763, mar 1561-1754, bur 1561-1763, **Ms 6419**, 18 vol.

1. 1561-1606/7	7. 1663-7	13. 1702/3-11
2. 1606/7-34	8. 1667-72	14. 1711-19/20
3. 1634/5-46	9. 1672-79/80	15. 1719/20-26/7
4. 1646-53	10. 1680-8	16. 1726/7-33
5. 1653-7	11. 1688-96	17. 1733-44
6. 1657-63	12. 1696-1702/3	18. bap 1744-63, mar 1744-54, bur 1744-63.

Note: bap entries 1646-1733 and bur entries 1665-1733 are marked either 'F' ('Freedom') or 'L' ('Lordship'), referring to the part of the parish in which the person baptised or buried was resident. The 'Freedom' was that part which lay within the City of London; the 'Lordship' was in the county of Middlesex. From 1733 to 1966 the 'Lordship' formed the separate parish of St Luke Old Street, the reg of which are now deposited at London Metropolitan Archives, 40 Northampton Road, London EC1R 0HB.

Index: **Boyd** (mar to 1625).

Bap and bur 1763-77, **Ms 6420/1**. Bur accounts from 1774, **in Ms 6095/1** (recording fees paid; some entries give addresses and ages of deceased).

Bap and bur 1777-92, **Ms 6420/2**. Bur accounts for these dates, **in Ms 6095/1** (recording fees paid; some entries give addresses and ages of deceased).

Bap and bur 1793-1807, **Ms 6420/3**. Bur accounts to 1793, **in Ms 6095/1** (recording fees paid; some entries give addresses and ages of deceased). Rough bap from 1806, **in Ms 6092/1** (entries apparently identical to those in Ms 6420/3). Index to bap in Ms 6420/3: **in Ms 6425/1**.

Bap and bur 1808-12, **Ms 6420/4**. Rough bap for these dates, **in Ms 6092/1** (entries apparently identical to those in Ms 6420/4). Index to bap in Ms 6420/4: **in Ms 6425/1**.

Bap 1813-17, **Ms 6423/1**. Rough bap 1813-14, **Ms 6092/2** (entries for these dates apparently identical to those in Ms 6423/1; also containing, at back, undated rough bap). Index to Ms 6423/1: **Ms 6425/2**.

Bap 1817-25, **Ms 6423/2**. Index: **Ms 6425/3**.

Bap 1825-33, **Ms 6423/3**. Rough bap 1827-33, **Ms 6092/3** (entries apparently identical to those in Ms 6423/3). Index to Ms 6423/3: **Ms 6425/4**.

Bap 1833-51, **Ms 6423/4**. Rough bap 1837-9, **Ms 6092/4** (entries apparently identical to those in Ms 6423/4). Index to Ms 6423/4: **Ms 6425/5**.

Bap 1851-1907 (with St. Bartholomew Moor Lane from 1901), **Ms 6423/5**. Indexed.

Bap 1907-61 (with St. Bartholomew Moor Lane; also, from 1954, with St Alphage London Wall and St Mary Aldermanbury), **Ms 6423/6**. Indexed to 1938.

Mar 1754-1837, **Ms 6421**, 6 vol.

1. 1754-81
2. 1781-98
3. 1798-1812
4. 1813-17
5. 1817-25
6. 1826-37.

Mar 1837-1953 and 1963-87 (with St Bartholomew Moor Lane from 1901, with St Alphage London Wall and St Mary Aldermanbury from 1963, and with St Luke Old Street, St Mary Charterhouse and St Paul Pear Tree Street from 1966), **Ms 6422**, 21 vol.

1. 1837-40
2. 1840-42
3. 1842-44
4. 1844-46
5. 1846-48
6. 1848-50
7. 1850-52
8. 1852-54
9. 1854-57
10. 1857-60
11. 1860-63
12. 1863-66
13. 1866-70
14. 1870-74
15. 1874-81
16. 1881-1936
17. 1937-53*
18. 1963-71
19. 1971-74
20. 1974-79
21. 1979-87.

*No mar solemnised 1953-63 during rebuilding of church.

Banns 1782-6, 1791-1832, 1838-1940 and 1976-82 (with St Bartholomew Moor Lane from 1901), **Ms 6093**, 15 vol.

1. 1782-86
2. 1791-96
3. 1796-1806
4. 1806-15
5. 1815-26
6. 1827-32
7. 1838-41
8. 1841-45
9. 1846-50
10. 1850-57
11. 1857-64
12. 1864-75
13. 1875-1936
14. 1937-40
15. 1976-82.

Rough banns 1801-3, 1808-15, 1848-78 and 1889-1938 (with St Bartholomew Moor Lane from 1901), **Ms 6094**, 7 vol.

1. 1801-03
2. 1808-10
3. 1810-15
4. 1848-59
5. 1859-78
6. 1889-1901
7. 1901-38.

Bur 1813-23, **Ms 6424/1**. Index: in J. Hanson and M. Stevens, *City of London burial index 1813-1853 part 3* (Milton Keynes, 1997?), fiches 104, **GL Printed Books Section**.

Bur 1823-37, **Ms 6424/2**. Duplicate bur 1828-34, **Ms 6095/2**. Bur accounts 1831-6, **Ms 6095/3** (incomplete), and from 1837, **in Ms 6095/5** (recording undertakers' names). Rough bur 1832-6, **Ms 6095/4** (omitting names of officiating ministers but, to July 1835, recording causes of death). Index to Ms 6424/2: in Hanson and Stevens, as above, **GL Printed Books Section**.

Bur 1838-53, **Ms 6424/3**. Bur accounts to 1843, **in Ms 6095/5**, and 1844-53, **in Ms 6095/6** (both recording undertakers' names). Supplementary bur 1845, **Ms 6095/7** (recording five bur of paupers, omitted from Ms 6424/3). Index to Ms 6424/3: in Hanson and Stevens, as above, **GL Printed Books Section**.

Funeral accounts 1854-1907, **in Ms 6095/6** (recording fees paid at funeral services held in the church after closure of the churchyard).

Certificate for interment of ashes 1929, **in Ms 6424/3**.

Later bap and mar reg retained by incumbent.

Transcripts:

B tr of bap 1813-37 and 1839, mar 1813-37, bur 1813-37 and 1839, **Ms 11340**, 5 boxes.

1. 1813-17
2. 1818-22
3. 1823-8
4. 1829-34
5. 1835-7 and 1839.

ST GREGORY BY ST PAUL

United to St Mary Magdalen Old Fish Street, 1670; St Martin Ludgate, 1890

Partial index to bap and mar in **IGI**.

Bap 1559-1627, mar 1559-1626/7, bur 1559-1627, **Ms 10231**. Index: **Boyd** (mar).

Bap 1627-51/2, mar 1627-35/6, bur 1627-59/60, **Ms 10232**. Index: **Boyd** (mar).

Bap 1652-86/7, mar 1636-40 and 1650/1-87, banns 1653-62, bur 1660-87, **Ms 10233**. Index: **Boyd** (mar).

Note: no mar solemnised 1641-50 during rebuilding of church.

Bap 1686/7-1717, mar 1687-1724, bur 1687-1726, **Ms 18932**. Rough births and bap 1695-1709, mar 1707-9, bur 1695-1708, **Ms 18933** (with some variant entries, and births of unbaptised children not found in Ms 18932). Index to mar in Ms 18932 and Ms 18933: **Boyd**.

Bap 1717-55, mar 1724-49, bur 1726-56, **Ms 18934**. Index to mar: **Boyd**.

Bap 1755-99, mar 1749-54, bur 1757-1800, **Ms 18935**. Index to mar: **Boyd**.

Bap 1799-1812, **Ms 18936/1**.

Bap 1813-56, **Ms 18936/2**. Index (compiled from b tr) 1813-21: **in Webb 4**.

Bap 1857-82, **Ms 18936/3**.

Mar and banns 1754-68, **Ms 18937/1**.

Mar 1768-81, banns 1768-78, **Ms 18937/2**.

Mar 1781-1800, **Ms 18937/3**.

Mar 1800-12, **Ms 18937/4**.

Mar 1813-37, **Ms 18937/5**. Index (compiled from b tr) 1813-21: **in Webb 4**.

Mar 1837-67, **Ms 18937/6**.

Bur 1800-12, **Ms 18938/1**.

Bur 1813-34, **Ms 18938/2**. Index (compiled from b tr) 1813-21: **in Webb 4 and 54/1-2**.

Bur 1834-53, **Ms 18938/3**.

For later bap, mar and banns, and for mar licences collection 1687-1834, see St Mary Magdalen Old Fish Street.

Transcripts:

Mar 1559-1754, **Challen 11**.

B tr of bap, mar and bur 1813-21, **Ms 11244** (tr and index **in Webb 4**).

ST HELEN BISHOPSGATE

Partial index to bap and mar in **IGI**.

Receipts for bur (with names of deceased) 1565-1654, in churchwardens' accounts, **in Ms 6836**.

Bap 1575-1700, mar 1575-1695, banns 1653-9, bur 1575-1686, entered in four vol, **Mss 6830/1-2** and **6831/1-2**, with much overlapping and duplication between 1598 and 1676, as follows:

Ms 6830/1: bap 1575-1649, mar 1575-1655, bur 1575-1651
Ms 6830/2: bap 1653-56/7 (Jan.), 1657 (Oct.-Nov.), 1664 (Sep.), 1665 (Apr.), 1666 (Jun.)-1672 (Jun.) and 1674/5 (Feb.), mar 1653-70 and 1676 (Dec.), banns 1653-9, bur 1653-70
Ms 6831/1: bap 1598-1654, mar 1606-53, bur 1598-1630
Ms 6831/2: bap 1649-1700, mar 1666-95, banns 1653 (Nov.-Dec.), bur 1651-86.

Where duplication is found, the bap entries are apparently identical in each reg; mar and bur entries vary in the amount of detail recorded, the most detailed entries being generally in Ms 6831/1-2. All four reg are transcribed, collated and indexed in **HS 31**; mar also indexed in **Boyd**. Mss 6830/1, 6831/2 also indexed in **Ms 23893/1-2** (bap) and **Ms 23894/ 1** (bur).

Mar 1695-1736, bur 1686-1736, **Ms 6832**. Indexes: **Boyd** (mar); **in HS 31** (mar and bur); **in Ms 23894/2** (bur).

Bap 1700-83, mar 1738-54, bur 1737-83, **Ms 6831/3**. Includes tr of bur 1783-1809 from Ms 6835/1. Indexes: **Boyd** (mar); **in HS 31** (bap, mar and bur); **in Ms 23893/2** (bap); **in Ms 23894/2** (bur).

Bap 1783-1809, **Ms 6833/1.** Indexes: **in HS 31**; **in Ms 23893/2**.

Bap 1809-13, **Ms 6833/2**. Indexes: **in HS 31**; **in Ms 23893/2**.

Bap 1813-1981 (with St Martin Outwich from 1873), **Ms 6833/3**. Indexes: **in Ms 23893/2** (to 1903); **in HS 31** (to 1837); **in Webb 3** (bap 1837-80 of persons born before 1841).

Mar 1754-80, banns 1754-77, **Ms 6834/1**. Indexes: **Boyd**; **in HS 31**.

Mar 1781-1812, **Ms 6834/2**. Indexes: **Boyd**; **in HS 31**.

Mar 1813-34, **Ms 6834/3**. Indexes: **Boyd**; **in HS 31**.

Mar 1834-7, **Ms 6834/4**. Indexes: **Boyd**; **in HS 31**.

Mar 1837-70, **Ms 6834/5**.

Later mar reg retained by incumbent.

Banns 1795-1821, **Ms 23895**.

Banns 1824-77 (with St Martin Outwich from c.1873), **Ms 6834A**.

Banns 1878-1993, also duplicate banns 1852-77 (all with St Martin Outwich from c.1873), **Ms 29288**.

Bur 1783-1809, **Ms 6835/1**. Indexes: **in HS 31**; **in Ms 23894/2**.

Bur 1809-1813, **Ms 6835/2**. Indexes: **in HS 31**; **in Ms 23894/2**.

Bur 1813-53, **Ms 6835/3**. Indexes: **in Ms 23894/2**; **in Webb 54/1-2**; **in HS 31** (to 1837); **in Webb 3** (1837-53).

Transcripts:

Bap, mar and bur 1575-1837, banns 1754-77, **HS 31**. Indexed.

Bur 1837-53, **Webb 3**. Indexed.

B tr of bap, mar and bur 1813-28, **Ms 11251/1**; bap 1829-81 (with St Martin Outwich from 1873), mar 1829-39, bur 1829-53, **Ms 11251/2**.

ST JAMES DUKE'S PLACE
United to St Katherine Cree, 1873

Partial index to bap and mar in **IGI**.

Bap 1747-1803, **Ms 7893/1**. Index: **in Webb 1**.

Bap 1803-12, **Ms 7893/2**. Index: **in Webb 1**.

Bap 1813-72, **Ms 7893/3**. Index: **in Webb 1** (to 1840).

Mar 1664-8 and 1678/9-91/2, **Ms 7894/1**. Index: **Boyd**.

Mar 1692-1700, **Ms 7894/2**. Index: **Boyd**.

Mar 1700-54, **Ms 7894/3**. Index: **Boyd**.

Mar 1754-72, **Ms 7894/4**. Index: **Boyd**.

Mar 1772-1800, banns 1772-1801, **Ms 7894/5**. Index: **Boyd** (mar).

Mar 1801-12, banns 1801-17, **Ms 7894/6**. Index: **Boyd** (mar).

Mar 1813-37, **Ms 7894/7**. Index: **Boyd**.

Mar 1838-68, **Ms 7894/8**.

Banns 1824-54, **Ms 7894A**.

Mar licences collection 1783-1866, **Ms 10938**.

Receipts for bur (with names of deceased) 1728-28/9, 1736-9 and 1743-60, in churchwardens' accounts, **in Ms 1218/1**.

Bur 1747-1812, **Ms 7895/1**. Index: **in Webb 1**.

Bur 1813-53, **Ms 7895/2**. Certificates of registry of death 1844-53, **Ms 7895A**. Index to Ms 7895/2: **in Webb 1 and 54/1-2**.

For later bap, mar, banns and mar licences see St Katherine Cree.

Transcripts:

Bap 1747-1840, bap 1841-57 of persons born before 1841, bur 1747-1853, **Webb 1**. Indexed.

Mar 1664-8 and 1678/9-1837, W.P.W. Phillimore and G.E. Cokayne, *Phillimore's parish register series, London 1-4*, 4 vol (London, 1900-2), **GL Printed Books Section**.

B tr of bap, mar and bur 1800-4, 1807-10, 1812 and 1814, **Ms 11173**.

ST JAMES GARLICKHITHE

Partial index to bap and mar in **IGI**.

Bap, mar and bur 1535-1692/3, **Ms 9140** (parchment book). Paper reg of bap, mar and bur 1535-83 and 1588/9-1621/2, **Ms 9138**, and 1622-66, **Ms 9139**, both recording some details omitted from entries in Ms 9140. Ms 9138 is evidently the original reg begun in 1535, but it is not known at what date the entries in this book were first copied into Ms 9140.

Bap, mar and bur 1693-1708: not extant.

Bap, mar and bur 1708-46, **Ms 9141**. Index: **Boyd** (mar).

Bap 1746-1809, mar 1746-54, bur 1746-1812, **Ms 9142**. Index: **Boyd** (mar).

Bap 1810-12, **Ms 9143/1**.

Bap 1813-54, **Ms 9143/2**.

Bap 1854-1971 (with St Michael Queenhithe and Holy Trinity the Less from 1876), **Ms 9143/3**.

Mar 1754-1807, banns 1754-73, **Ms 9144/1**. Index: **in Webb 16 and 40**.

Mar 1807-12, **Ms 9144/2**. Index: **in Webb 16 and 40**.

Mar 1813-37, **in Ms 9144/3**. Index: **in Webb 16 and 40**.

Mar 1837-1970 (with St Michael Queenhithe and Holy Trinity the Less from 1875), **Ms 21759**. Mar 1837-50 also entered **in Ms 9144/3**, and mar 1850-68 in **Ms 9144/4**, but in less detail than in Ms 21759.

Banns 1773-1816, **Ms 9145**.

Banns 1823-52 and 1950 (one entry for St James Garlickhithe with St Michael Queenhithe and Holy Trinity the Less), **Ms 22272**.

Mar licences collection 1810-1933, **Ms 9162**. Index: **in Ms 24657** (to 1838).

Bur 1813-47, **Ms 9146/1**. Index: **in Webb 54/1-2**.

Bur 1847-53, **Ms 9146/2**. Index: **in Webb 54/1-2**.

Transcripts:

Bap, mar and bur 1535-8, W.D. Cooper, *London and Middlesex Archaeological Society Transactions*, vol 3 (1870), pp 392-6, **GL Printed Books Section**.

Mar 1535-1692 and 1708-54, **Challen 27**.

Mar 1754-1837, banns 1754-73, **Webb 16**. Index: **in Webb 16** (places) **and 40** (names).

B tr of bap, mar and bur 1630-30/1, **in Ms 10107**; bap, mar and bur 1639-39/40, **in Ms 10107A**; bap, mar and bur 1800-40, **Ms 11246**; bap 1840-5, 1847-51, 1853-60, 1862-5, 1876 and 1881-90, mar 1840-5, 1847-51, 1853-60 and 1862-5, bur 1840-5, 1847-51 and 1853, **Ms 11247**.

ST JAMES IN THE WALL:- see LAMB'S CHAPEL

ST JOHN THE BAPTIST WALBROOK
United to St Antholin Budge Row, 1670; St Mary Aldermary, 1873

Partial index to bap in **IGI**.

Receipts for bur (with names of deceased) in churchwardens' accounts 1595-1679, **in Ms 577/1**; 1679-80, **in Ms 577/2**.

B tr of bap, mar and bur 1629-29/30, **in Ms 10107**. Index: **in Webb 7**.

Bap 1682 and 1686-1812, bur 1686-1812, **Ms 9021**. Indexes: **in HS 8** (to1754); **in Webb 7** (1754-1812).

For later bap and bur, and for mar from c.1670, see St Antholin Budge Row.

Transcripts:

Bap, mar and bur 1629-29/30 (from b tr), and bap and bur 1754-1812, **Webb 7**. Indexed.

Bap 1682 and 1686-1754, bur 1686-1754, **HS 8**. Indexed.

B tr of bap, mar and bur 1629-29/30, **in Ms 10107**; bap and bur 1800-5, 1807 and 1809-12, **Ms 11161** (also containing b tr of mar 1801 and 1803-5, from reg of St Antholin Budge Row with St John the Baptist Walbrook).

ST JOHN THE EVANGELIST FRIDAY STREET
United to Allhallows Bread Street, 1670; St Mary le Bow, 1876

Partial index to bap in **IGI**.

Bap 1653-1723, mar 1653-66, bur 1653-1723, **Ms 5041**. Indexes: **Boyd** (mar); **in HS 43** (bap, mar and bur).

Bap and bur 1723-1812, **Ms 5042**. Some rough bap and bur from 1789, **in Ms 5034** (includes rough bap and bur of Allhallows Bread Street). Index to Ms 5042: **in HS 43**.

Bap 1813-21, **Ms 5043**. Some rough bap to 1820, **in Ms 5034**. Index to Ms 5043: **in HS 43**.

Bur 1813-22, **Ms 5044**. Rough bur to 1820, **in Ms 5034** (entries from 1816 record some details not found in Ms 5044). Indexes to Ms 5044: **in HS 43**; **in Webb 54/1-2**.

For later reg see Allhallows Bread Street.

Transcripts:

Bap 1653-1821, mar 1653-66, bur 1653-1822, **HS 43**. Indexed.

B tr of bap and bur 1813-16, **Ms 11239B**. For later b tr see Allhallows Bread Street. Note: b tr of bap, mar and bur 1799, 1802 and 1804-11 are held by Lambeth Palace Library, London SE1 7JU.

ST JOHN ZACHARY

United to St Anne and St Agnes, 1670; St Vedast Foster Lane, 1954

Partial index to bap and mar in **IGI**.

Receipts for bur (with names of deceased) in churchwardens' accounts 1591-1682, **in Ms 590/1**; 1683-1723, **in Ms 590/2**.

B tr of bap, mar and bur 1665-65/6, **in Ms 10952**. Index: **in Webb 40** (mar).

Bap and bur 1693-1812, **Ms 6769**. Rough bap and bur 1788-92, **in Ms 6773A** (some entries omitted; others apparently identical to those in Ms 6769). Rough bap and bur 1796-8, **in Ms 6773B** (entries apparently identical to those in Ms 6769). Indexes to Ms 6769: **in Ms 6772B/1** (bap A-H); **in Ms 6772B/2** (bap I-Z); **in Ms 6772B/4** (bur).

Bap 1813-95, **Ms 6770**. Indexes (to 1837): **in Ms 6772B/1** (A-H); **in Ms 6772B/2** (I-Z).

Mar 1755-1812, banns 1755-65, **Ms 6771/1**. Indexes: in reg (mar); **in Ms 6772B/3** (mar); **in Webb 40** (mar).

Mar 1813-37, **Ms 6771/2**. Indexes: in reg; **in Ms 6772B/3; in Webb 40**.

Bur 1813-49, **Ms 6772**. Indexes: **in Webb 54/1-2; in Ms 6772B/4** (to 1837).

For later reg (bap from 1896, mar from 1837, banns from 1774), and for mar licences from 1831, see St Anne and St Agnes.

Transcripts:

Mar 1665-65/6 and 1755-1837, **Webb 40**. Indexed.

Bap 1693-1812, **Ms 3701/36**.

Bur 1693-1812, **Ms 3701/38**.

B tr of bap, mar and bur 1665-65/6, **in Ms 10952**; bap 1800-1, 1807-46 and 1848-50, mar 1800-1 and 1807-37, bur 1800-1, 1807-45 and 1849, **Ms 11172**.

ST KATHERINE COLEMAN
United to St Olave Hart Street, 1921

Partial index to bap and mar in **IGI**.

Bap 1559-1666, mar 1563-1666, bur 1559-1666, **Ms 17832** (two vol bound in one: the first contains bap 1559-1659, mar 1563-1658/9 and bur 1559-1648; the second contains dates of birth 1653-8, bap 1658-66, banns and mar 1653-6, mar 1658-66 and bur 1653-66). Index to mar: **Boyd**.

Bap 1666-1741, mar 1666-1738, bur 1666-1741/2, **Ms 17833**. Bur accounts from 1734, **in Ms 17837A** (some entries contain details not found in Ms 17833). Index to mar: **Boyd**.

Bap 1741-1812, **Ms 17834/1**. Duplicate bap 1741-63, **in Ms 17835/1**.

Bap 1813-74, **Ms 17834/2**.

Bap 1874-1914, **Ms 17834/3**.

No mar solemnised 1738-41 during rebuilding of church.

Mar 1741-1920, **Ms 17835**, 7 vol. Index: **Boyd** (to 1754).

1. 1741-54	3. 1797-99*	5. 1813-32	7. 1837-1920.
2. 1754-97	4. 1800-12*	6. 1833-7	

*one mar 1804 **in Ms 17835/3**.

Banns 1754-1916, **Ms 17836**, 3 vol.

1. 1754-1807	2. 1807-45	3. 1845-1916.

Mar licences collection 1760-1872, **Ms 7725**. Index: **in Ms 24657** (to 1838).

Bur 1742-1812: no reg extant. Bur accounts for these dates, **in Ms 17837A**.

Bur 1813-53, **Ms 17837**. Bur accounts to 1833, **in Ms 17837A** (frequently omitting addresses, but some entries contain other details not found in Ms 17837). Index to Ms 17837: **in Webb 54/1-2**.

For later bap, mar and banns see St Olave Hart Street.

Transcripts:

Mar 1563-1754, **Challen 12**.

B tr of bap, mar and bur 1629-30/1, **in Ms 10107**; bap, mar and bur 1665-66/7, **in Ms 10952**; bap, mar and bur 1802, 1807-10 and 1812, **Ms 11171**; bap 1813-52, mar 1813-37, bur 1813-52, **Ms 11171A**.

ST KATHERINE CREE

Partial index to bap and mar in **IGI**.

B tr of bap, mar and bur 1639-39/40, **in Ms 10107A**. Index to mar: **in Webb 17 and 40**.

Receipts for bur (with names of deceased) 1650-61, in churchwardens' accounts, **in Ms 1198/1**.

Bap 1663-92/3, mar and bur 1663-93, **Ms 7889/1**. Index to mar: **in Webb 17 and 40**.

Bap 1692/3-1722, mar and bur 1693-1722, **Ms 7889/2**. Index to mar: **in Webb 17 and 40**.

Bap 1722-58, mar and bur 1722-54, **in Ms 7889/3**. Index to mar: **in Webb 17 and 40**.

Bap 1758-98, bur 1754-98, **Ms 7890/1**. Rough bur 1754-8, **in Ms 7889/3** (with some variant entries).

Bap and bur 1798-1812, **Ms 7890/2**.

Bap 1813-1947 (with St James Duke's Place from 1873), **Ms 9368**.

Mar 1754-85, **Ms 7891/1**. Mar 1754-8 also entered in abbreviated form **in Ms 7889/3** (with some variant entries). Index to Ms 7891/1: **in Webb 17 and 40**.

Mar 1785-1810, **Ms 7891/2**. Index: **in Webb 17 and 40**.

Mar 1810-12, **Ms 7891/3**. Index: **in Webb 17 and 40**.

Mar 1813-37, **in Ms 7891/4**. Index: **in Webb 17 and 40**.

Mar 1837-1903 (with St James Duke's Place from 1874), **Ms 7891/5**. Mar 1837-8 also entered **in Ms 7891/4**.

Mar 1904-33 (with St James Duke's Place), **Ms 7891/6**.

Rough banns 1812-16, **Ms 7901**.

Banns 1824-35, **Ms 7902**.

Banns 1874-1950 (with St James Duke's Place), **Ms 9369**.

Mar licences collection 1780-1805, **Ms 7709**. Index: **in Ms 24657**.

Mar licences collection 1876-99 (with St James Duke's Place), **Ms 10935**.

Bur 1813-53, **Ms 7892**. Bur accounts 1818-31, **Ms 1200/1**; 1831-43, **Ms 1200/2**; 1843-53, **in Ms 1200/3**. Index to Ms 7892: in J. Hanson and M. Stevens, *City of London burial index 1813-1853 part 3* (Milton Keynes, 1997?), fiches 104, **GL Printed Books Section**.

Funeral accounts 1853-70, **in Ms 1200/3** (recording names of deceased and of undertakers, and fees paid for ringing the bell at funeral services held in the church after the closure of the churchyard).

Later bap and mar reg retained by incumbent.

Transcripts:

Mar 1639-39/40 (from b tr) and 1663-1837, **Webb 17**. Index: **in Webb 17** (places) **and 40** (names).

B tr of bap, mar and bur 1639-39/40, **in Ms 10107A**; bap, mar and bur 1664-64/5, **in Ms 10952**; bap 1800 and 1803-12, mar 1800, 1803, 1804 (incomplete) and 1805-12, bur 1800 and 1803-12, **Ms 11178**; bap 1813-63, mar 1813-37, bur 1813-53, **Ms 11178A**.

ST LAWRENCE JEWRY

Partial index to bap and mar in **IGI**.

Bap, mar and bur 1538-1715 (with St Mary Magdalen Milk Street from c.1670), **in Ms 6975**. Entries to 1598 in this reg are parchment copies. Original paper reg of bap 1538-1605 and mar and bur 1538-1604, **Ms 6974**. Indexes: **Boyd** (mar); **in HS 70-1** (bap, mar and bur).

Note: Ms 6975 includes mar 1668/9-1701/2 and bur 1669-77 at Guildhall Chapel.

Bap 1715-87, mar 1715-54, bur 1715/6-1812 (all with St Mary Magdalen Milk Street), **Ms 6976**. Indexes: **Boyd** (mar); **in HS 71** (bap, mar and bur).

Bap 1787-1812 (with St Mary Magdalen Milk Street), **Ms 6980**. Indexes: **in HS 71**; **in Ms 3292**.

Bap 1813-1940 (with St Mary Magdalen Milk Street; also, from c.1897, with St Michael Bassishaw): reg damaged beyond repair by enemy action in 1940. B tr of bap 1813-25, 1837-42 and 1845-6, **in Ms 10442A** (indexed 1813-25 and 1837-42 in **Webb 6**). Tr of extracts from bap 1880 and 1908, in **Ms 3713/1**.

Bap 1941-53 (with St Mary Magdalen Milk Street and St Michael Bassishaw), **Ms 23942**.

Mar 1754-94, banns 1754-62 (both with St Mary Magdalen Milk Street), **Ms 6977**. Indexes: in reg (mar and banns, males only); **Boyd** (mar to 1764); **in HS 71** (mar); **in Ms 3292** (mar and banns).

Mar 1794-1812 (with St Mary Magdalen Milk Street), **Ms 6981**. Indexes: in reg (males only); **in HS 71**; **in Ms 3292**.

Mar 1813-1928 and 1938-51 (with St Mary Magdalen Milk Street; also, from c.1897, with St Michael Bassishaw), **Ms 6978**, 5 vol. Index: **in Webb 6** (1813-37).

1. 1813-37 3. 1925-8 5. 1945-51.
2. 1837-1924 4. 1938-40

Note: reg containing mar 1928-38 destroyed by enemy action in 1940; duplicate reg deposited at the London City Register Office, Finsbury Town Hall, Rosebery Avenue, London EC1R 4QT.

Mar 1957-83 (with St Mary Magdalen Milk Street and St Michael Bassishaw), **Ms 23943**, 4 vol.

1. 1957-63 2. 1963-8 3. 1968-73 4. 1974-83.

Banns 1764-1803 (with St Mary Magdalen Milk Street), **Ms 2517**.

Banns 1803-73 (with St Mary Magdalen Milk Street), **Ms 6982**.

Banns 1875-1933 (with St Mary Magdalen Milk Street; also, from c.1897, with St Michael Bassishaw), **Ms 6983**.

Bur 1813-53 (with St Mary Magdalen Milk Street), **Ms 6979**. Index: **in Webb 6 and 54/1-2**.

Later bap and mar reg retained by incumbent.

Transcripts:

Bap, mar and bur 1538-1676, **HS 70**. Indexed.

Bap, mar and bur 1677-1812, **HS 71**. Indexed.

Mar 1538-1764, **Challen 9**.

Bap 1813-25 and 1837-42 (from b tr), mar 1813-37 and bur 1813-53, **Webb 6**. Indexed.

B tr of bap, mar and bur 1800-3, 1805 (Apr.)-1806 (Apr.) and 1807-1812, **Ms 10442**; bap 1813-25, 1837-42 and 1845-6, mar 1813-25 and 1837, bur 1813-25, 1837-42 and 1845-6, **Ms 10442A**.

ST LAWRENCE POUNTNEY
United to St Mary Abchurch, 1670

Partial index to bap and mar in **IGI**.

Receipts for bur (with names of deceased) 1530-49 and 1619-81, in churchwardens' accounts, **in Ms 3907/1**.

Bap 1538-1739/40, mar 1538/9-1666, banns 1654-9, bur 1538-1739/40, **Ms 7670**. Reg of affidavits of bur in woollen 1678-1738, **Ms 7671** (recording dates of affidavits but omitting addresses and names of parents, husbands etc). Index to mar and banns: **Boyd**.

For bap and bur from 1740, see St Mary Abchurch.

For mar from c.1670, see St Mary Abchurch. One mar 1715/6, **in Ms 7670**.

Banns 1757-62 and 1804-1953: see St Mary Abchurch.

Transcripts:

Mar 1538/9-1666 and 1813-37, **Challen 13**.

B tr of bap, mar and bur 1629-30/1, **in Ms 10107**; bap, mar and bur 1639-39/40, **in Ms 10107A**; bap and bur 1802, 1803 (Apr.)-1804 (Apr.), 1804 (Oct.)-1806 (May) and 1808-12, **Ms 10423** (also containing b tr of mar 1802, 1803 (Apr.)-1804 (Apr.), 1805-6 (May) and 1809-12, from reg of St Mary Abchurch with St Lawrence Pountney); bap, mar and bur 1813-21 and 1823, **Ms 10423B**.

ST LEONARD EASTCHEAP
United to St Benet Gracechurch, 1670; Allhallows Lombard Street, 1864; St Edmund the King and Martyr, 1937

Partial index to bap and mar in **IGI**.

Bap 1538-1752, mar 1538-1705, bur 1538-1752, **Ms 17607**. Index: **Boyd** (mar).

Bap and bur 1752-1812, **Ms 17608**. Rough bap 1795-8 and bur 1795-9, **in Ms 5672** (entries apparently identical to those in Ms 17608). Rough bur 1801-13, **Ms 5675** (some entries record, besides details in Ms 17608, causes of death).

For later reg see St Benet Gracechurch.

Transcripts:

Mar 1538-1705, **Challen 6**.

Note: b tr of bap, mar and bur 1802, 1804-5 and 1807-12 are held by Lambeth Palace Library, London SE1 7JU.

ST LEONARD FOSTER LANE

United to Christchurch Newgate Street, 1670; St Sepulchre Holborn, 1954

B tr of bap, mar and bur 1639-39/40, **in Ms 10107A**.

For bap, mar and bur from c.1670 see Christchurch Newgate Street.

ST MAGNUS THE MARTYR

Partial index to bap and mar in **IGI**.

Bap 1560/1-1719/20, mar 1557/8-1712, bur 1560/1-1720/1 (all with St Margaret New Fish Street from c.1670), **Ms 11361**. Rough bap 1669-89/90, mar 1675-90, bur 1669-85 and 1686/7-89, **Ms 8786** (some entries omitted, but including other names not found in Ms 11361; many bur entries record more details than Ms 11361). Rough bap 1690-1703 and bur 1689-1700, **Ms 8787** (bap entries apparently identical to those in Ms 11361; many bur entries record more details). Dates of birth 1696-1706, rough mar 1700/1-6 and 1716, rough bur 1696-1706 and 1715-16, **Ms 8788** (mar and bur entries apparently identical to those in Ms 11361). Bur accounts 1701-7, **Ms 2789**. Indexes to Ms 11361: **Boyd** (mar); also **in Ms 11366**, 10 vol, for which see list below.

Bap 1719/20-1812, mar 1712-54, bur 1720/1-1812 (all with St Margaret New Fish Street), **Ms 11362** (photocopy on Reading Room shelves, **Ms 11362A**). Rough mar 1716, **in Ms 8788**. Rough bap 1721-68 and mar 1722-4 and 1726-54, **Ms 8789** (entries apparently identical to those in Ms 11362). Bur accounts 1744-78, **Ms 8314**. Indexes to Ms 11362: **Boyd** (mar); also **in Ms 11366**, 10 vol, for which see list below.

Bap 1813-1978 (with St Margaret New Fish Street from 1813 and St Michael Crooked Lane from 1890), **Ms 21748**. Index (to 1891): **in Ms 11366/8**.

Mar 1754-99, banns 1754-7 (both with St Margaret New Fish Street), **Ms 11363/1**. Indexes: **Boyd** (to 1775); **in Ms 11366/6** (mar).

Mar 1799-1812 (with St Margaret New Fish Street), **Ms 11363/2**. Indexes: **Boyd** (from 1801); **in Ms 11366/6** (1799); **in Ms 11366/9** (from 1800).

Mar 1813-37 (with St Margaret New Fish Street), **Ms 11363/3**. Indexes: **Boyd**; **in Ms 11366/9**.

Mar 1838-1991 (with St Margaret New Fish Street and St Michael Crooked Lane), **Ms 11363/4**. Index: **in Ms 11366/9** (to 1891).

Banns 1793-1952 (with St Margaret New Fish Street from 1793 and St Michael Crooked Lane from c.1840), **Ms 11364**. Some banns 1840-1949, omitted from Ms 11364, **in Ms 11371**. Index to banns 1801-37: **Boyd**.

Mar licences collection 1827-1900 (with St Margaret New Fish Street from 1827 and St Michael Crooked Lane from 1831), **Ms 21749**. Index: **in Ms 24657** (to 1838).

Bur 1813-53 (with St Margaret New Fish Street), **Ms 11365**. Indexes: **in Ms 11366/10**; **in Webb 54/1-2**.

Transcripts:

Mar 1557/8-1712, **Challen 7**.

Mar 1712-1837, banns 1754-7 and 1793-1837, **Challen 22**.

B tr of bap, mar and bur 1800-12 (with St Margaret New Fish Street), **Ms 11175**; bap 1813-50, mar 1813-37 and 1842-50, bur 1813-50 (all with St Margaret New Fish Street; mar also with St Michael Crooked Lane from 1842), **Ms 11175A**.

Indexes 1557/8-1891, **Ms 11366,** 10 vol.

1. Bap 1560/1-99, mar 1557/8-99, bur 1560/1-99
2. Bap 1600-99
3. Mar 1600-99
4. Bur 1600-99
5. Bap 1700-99
6. Mar 1700-99
7. Bur 1700-99
8. Bap 1800-91, with index to bap of St Michael Crooked Lane
9. Mar 1800-91, with index to mar of St Michael Crooked Lane
10. Bur 1800-53, with index to bur of St Michael Crooked Lane.

ST MARGARET LOTHBURY

Partial index to bap and mar in **IGI**.

Bap 1558-1736/7, mar 1558-1735/6, bur 1558-1736, **Ms 4346/1**. Index: **Boyd** (mar).

Bap 1736/7-74, mar 1735/6-54, bur 1736-74, **Ms 4346/2**. Index: **Boyd** (mar).

Bap and bur 1774-1812 (with St Christopher le Stocks from 1781), **Ms 4348**.

Bap 1813-1924 (with St Christopher le Stocks from 1813, with St Bartholomew by the Exchange from 1841, and with St Olave Jewry, St Martin Pomeroy, St Mildred Poultry and St Mary Colechurch from c.1886), **Ms 8847**.

Later bap reg retained by incumbent.

Mar 1754-75, **Ms 4347/1**. Index: **in Webb 16 and 40**.

Mar 1775-1812 (with St Christopher le Stocks from 1781), **Ms 4347/2**. Index: **in Webb 16 and 40**.

Mar 1813-37 (with St Christopher le Stocks), **Ms 8848**. Index: **in Webb 16 and 40**.

Mar 1837-1996 (with St Christopher le Stocks, with St Bartholomew by the Exchange from c.1840, and with St Olave Jewry, St Martin Pomeroy, St Mildred Poultry and St Mary Colechurch from c.1886), **Ms 31353**. One mar 1875, **in Ms 4346/2**.

Banns 1774-1899 (with St Christopher le Stocks from 1781, with St Bartholomew by the Exchange from c.1841, and with St Olave Jewry, St Martin Pomeroy, St Mildred Poultry and St Mary Colechurch from c.1886), **Ms 4350**.

Banns 1945, **in Ms 4433**.

Mar licences collection 1753-1918 and 1971 (with St Christopher le Stocks from 1781, with St Bartholomew by the Exchange from c.1841, and with St Olave Jewry, St Martin Pomeroy, St Mildred Poultry and St Mary Colechurch from c.1886), **Ms 24135**. Index: **in Ms 24657** (to 1838).

Bur 1813-53 (with St Christopher le Stocks from 1813, and with St Bartholomew by the Exchange from 1841), **Ms 4349**. Certificates of registry of death 1826-52, **Ms 4349A**. Index to Ms 4349: **in Webb 54/1-2**.

Transcripts:

Mar 1558-1754, **Challen 8**.

Mar 1754-1837, **Webb 16**. Index: **in Webb 16** (places) **and 40** (names).

B tr of bap and bur 1665-65/6, **in Ms 10952**; bap 1800-2 and 1807-55, mar 1800-2 and 1807-40, bur 1800-2 and 1807-53, **Ms 4350A**.

ST MARGARET MOSES

United to St Mildred Bread Street, 1670; St Mary le Bow, 1954

Partial index to bap and mar in **IGI**.

Bap 1559-1812, **Ms 3479**. Index: **in HS 42**.

Bap 1814-1938: reg destroyed by enemy action in 1941. Tr and index of bap to 1837, **in HS 42**. B tr of bap 1814-28 and 1832-42, **in Ms 11176A** (indexed 1838-42 **in Webb 3**).

Mar 1558-1665, **in Ms 3480**. Indexes: **Boyd**; **in HS 42**.

Mar 1670-1812, banns 1754-74: see St Mildred Bread Street.

Mar 1813-36, **Ms 3481**. Indexes: **Boyd**; **in HS 42**.

Mar 1837-1939: reg destroyed by enemy action in 1941. Four mar 1837-9 entered **in Ms 3481**.

Bur 1558-1812, **in Ms 3480**. Index: **in HS 42**.

Bur 1813-50, **Ms 3482**. Indexes: **in HS 42**; **in Webb 54/1-2**.

Transcripts:

Bap 1559-1837, mar 1558-1666 and 1813-36, bur 1558-1850, **HS 42**. Indexed.

Bap 1559-1812, mar 1558-1666, bur 1558-1812, **Ms 12003**.

B tr of bap and bur 1665-6, **in Ms 10952**; bap, mar (from reg of St Mildred Bread Street with St Margaret Moses) and bur 1800-12, **Ms 11176**; bap 1814-28 and 1832-42, mar 1813-29 and 1832-7, bur 1813-29 and 1832-42, **Ms 11176A**.

ST MARGARET NEW FISH STREET

United to St Magnus the Martyr, 1670

Receipts for bur (with names of deceased) 1577-1678, in churchwardens' accounts, **in Ms 1176/1**.

B tr of bap, mar and bur 1629-30/1, **in Ms 10107**; 1639-39/40, **in Ms 10107A**. Tr and index: **Webb 4**.

For reg from c.1670 see St Magnus the Martyr.

ST MARGARET PATTENS

Partial index to bap and mar in **IGI**.

Bap 1559-1653, mar 1559-1660, bur 1558-1653, **Ms 5287/1**. Indexes: **Boyd** (mar); **in Webb 16 and 40** (mar from 1650/1).

Bap 1653-1812, banns 1653-7, mar 1660-1754 (with St Gabriel Fenchurch from c.1683/4), bur 1653-1812, **Ms 5287/2**. Index: **in Webb 16 and 40** (banns and mar).

Bap 1813-1952 (with St Gabriel Fenchurch from c.1901), **Ms 5288**.

Mar 1754-1804 (with St Gabriel Fenchurch), **Ms 5289/1**. Index: **in Webb 16 and 40**.

Mar 1804-12 (with St Gabriel Fenchurch), **Ms 5289/2**. Index: **in Webb 16 and 40**.

Mar 1813-37, **Ms 5290/1**. Index: **in Webb 16 and 40**.

Mar 1837-1952 (with St Gabriel Fenchurch), **Ms 5290/2**.

Banns 1754-1823 (with St Gabriel Fenchurch), **Ms 5292/1**.

Banns 1824-50 (with St Gabriel Fenchurch), **Ms 5292/2**.

Banns 1852-81 (with St Gabriel Fenchurch), **Ms 9346**.

Bur 1813-53, **Ms 5291**. Index: **in Webb 54/1-2**.

Transcripts:

Mar 1650/1-1837, banns 1653-7, **Webb 16**. Index: **in Webb 16** (places) **and 40** (names).

B tr of bap 1800-1, 1807-10 (Mar.) and 1811-12, mar 1800-1, 1803-4 (with St Gabriel Fenchurch), 1807-10 (Mar.) and 1811-12, bur 1800-1, 1807-10 (Mar.) and 1811-12, **Ms 10427**; bap 1813-33 and 1840, mar 1813-33, bur 1813-33 and 1840 (all with St Gabriel Fenchurch), **Ms 10427A**. Note: St Gabriel mar 1832 missing.

ST MARTIN LUDGATE

Partial index to bap in **IGI**.

Bap 1538/9-1719, mar 1538-1715, bur 1538-1719, entered in two vol, **Mss 10212 and 10213**, with some overlapping, as follows:

Ms 10212: bap 1538/9-1654/5, mar 1538-1653, bur 1538-1655

Ms 10213: bap 1558-1719, mar 1559-1715, bur 1558-1719

(Ms 10212 is the original paper reg, and entries to 1599 in the parchment book Ms 10213 are copies from it. For the years in which the two vol overlap, the entries in each are apparently identical). Index: **Boyd** (mar 1626-1700).

(Note: entries in Ms 10213 are in disorder - see note at front of vol concerning arrangement of contents.)

Bap 1719-1812, mar 1715-54, bur 1719/20-1812, **Ms 10214**. Rough bap and bur 1765-91, **Ms 23903/1**; rough bap and bur 1792-1812, **in Ms 23903/2** (entries apparently identical to those in Ms 10214).

Bap 1813-1929 (with St Mary Magdalen Old Fish Street and St Gregory by St Paul from 1895), **Ms 10215**.

Mar 1754-1953 (with St Mary Magdalen Old Fish Street and St Gregory by St Paul from 1895), **Ms 10216,** 4 vol. Index: **in Webb 17 and 40** (to 1837).

1. 1754-95 2. 1796-1812 3. 1813-37 4. 1837-1953.

Banns 1754-1831, **Ms 10217**.

Banns 1832-89, **Ms 18940**.

Banns 1890-1958 (with St Mary Magdalen Old Fish Street and St Gregory by St Paul), **in Ms 23904**.

Bur 1813-48, **Ms 10218**. Rough bur to 1814, **in Ms 23903/2** (entries apparently identical to those in Ms 10218). Bur accounts for these dates, **in Ms 1326**. Index to Ms 10218: in J. Hanson and M. Stevens, *City of London burial index 1813-1853 part 3* (Milton Keynes, 1997?), fiches 104, **GL Printed Books Section**.

Funeral accounts 1848-50, **in Ms 1326** (recording fees paid for funeral services held in the church after closure of the vaults).

One funeral 1909, **in Ms 10218**.

Later bap and mar reg retained by incumbent.

Transcripts:

Mar 1538-1754, **Challen 12**.

Mar 1754-1837, **Webb 17**. Index: **in Webb 17** (places) **and 40** (names).

B tr of bap, mar and bur 1629-29/30, **in Ms 10107**; bap, mar and bur 1639-40, **in Ms 10107A**; bap, mar and bur 1800-12, **Ms 10429**; bap, mar and bur 1813-37, **Ms 10429A**; bap 1838-72, bur 1838-48, **Ms 10429B**.

ST MARTIN ORGAR

United to St Clement Eastcheap, 1670

Partial index to bap and mar in **IGI**.

Bap 1625-1812, mar 1625-87, bur 1624-1812, **Ms 4784**. Includes one mar 1734 and one mar 1738 (all other mar from 1688 entered in reg of St Clement Eastcheap). Indexes: **Boyd** (mar); **in HS 68**.

For later reg see St Clement Eastcheap.

Transcripts:

Bap 1625-1812, mar 1625-87, 1734 and 1738, bur 1624-1812, **HS 68**. Indexed.

Mar 1625-87, 1734 and 1738, **Challen 6**.

B tr of bap and bur 1629-30/1, **in Ms 10107**; bap, mar and bur 1639-39/40, **in Ms 10107A**; bap and bur 1801-8, **Ms 11177A**. For later b tr see St Clement Eastcheap.

Note: reg of the French church at St Martin Orgar 1698-1762 have been transcribed in *Publications of the Huguenot Society of London*, vol 37 (1935), **GL Printed Books Section**.

ST MARTIN OUTWICH

United to St Helen Bishopsgate, 1873

Partial index to bap and mar in **IGI**.

Receipts for bur (with names of deceased) 1632-1742, in churchwardens' accounts, **in Ms 11394/1**.

B tr of bap 1664-64/5, **in Ms 10952**. Index: **in Webb 4**.

Bap 1670-1795, mar 1670-1754, bur 1670-1795, **Ms 6837**. Indexes: **Boyd** (mar); **in HS 32** (bap, mar and bur).

Bap and bur 1796-1812, **in Ms 6838/1**. Includes tr of bap and bur 1813-19 from Ms 6838/2 and Ms 6840 respectively. Index: **in HS 32**.

Bap 1813-73, **Ms 6838/2**. Tr (contemporary) of bap 1813-19, **in Ms 6838/1** (with some additional details). Index (to 1873): **in HS 32**.

For later bap see St Helen Bishopsgate.

Mar 1754-1812, banns 1755-76, **Ms 6839/1**. Indexes: **Boyd**; **in HS 32**.

Mar 1813-37, **in Ms 6839/2**. Includes mar 1837-55, as in Ms 6839/3 (with less detail; giving parishes rather than precise addresses of parties). Indexes: **Boyd** (to 1837); **in HS 32**.

Mar 1837-72, **Ms 6839/3**. Index: **in HS 32**.

Banns 1824-72, **Ms 6841**. Indexes: **Boyd** (to 1837); **in HS 32**.

For later banns see St Helen Bishopsgate.

Mar licences collection 1716 and 1817-50, **Ms 11424**. Index: **in Ms 24657** (to 1838).

Bur 1813-52, **Ms 6840**. Indexes: **in HS 32**; **in Webb 54/1-2**.

Later mar entered in reg of St Helen Bishopsgate (retained by incumbent).

Transcripts:

Bap 1664-4/5 (from b tr), **Webb 4**. Indexed.

Bap 1670-1873, mar 1670-1872, banns 1755-76 and 1824-72, bur 1670-1852, **HS 32**. Indexed.

B tr of bap 1664-64/5, **in Ms 10952**; bap, mar and bur 1802-33, **Ms 11338**.

ST MARTIN POMEROY

United to St Olave Jewry, 1670; St Margaret Lothbury, 1886

Partial index to bap and mar in **IGI**.

Bap 1539-1812, births of non-conformists' children 1690-7, mar 1539-1647/8, bur 1539-1812, **Ms 4392**. Index: **Boyd** (mar).

Bap 1813-18, **Ms 4394**. Tr **in Ms 4393**.

Bur 1813-17, **Ms 4395**. Tr **in Ms 4393**.

Bap 1819-85, bur 1818-47, **Ms 4393**. Includes tr of bap 1813-18 and bur 1813-17, from Ms 4394 and Ms 4395 respectively. Index to Ms 4393: **in Webb 54/1-2** (bur).

For bap from c.1886 see St Margaret Lothbury; for mar from c.1670 and banns from 1771 see St Olave Jewry.

Transcripts:

Mar 1539-1647/8, **Challen 8**.

B tr of bap and bur 1801 and 1807-12, **Ms 10430** (also containing b tr of mar 1807-11 from reg of St Olave Jewry with St Martin Pomeroy). For later b tr see St Olave Jewry.

ST MARTIN VINTRY

United to St Michael Paternoster Royal, 1670

Partial index to bap and mar in **IGI**.

Reg to 1664 presumed lost in the Great Fire. Some rough bap, mar and bur 1617-49, with some undated entries 1649-64, **Ms 9301**. B tr of bap, mar and bur 1629-30/1, **in Ms 10107**, and 1639-39/40, **in Ms 10107A** (both indexed **in Webb 4**).

Bap 1664 and 1669/70-1722, mar 1675-1710 (with St Michael Paternoster Royal), bur 1668-1722, **Ms 5152**. Rough bap 1665, 1669/70-83 (Jun.) and 1684 (Apr.)-1719, mar 1702, bur 1668-83 (Oct.) and 1684 (Jul.)-1719, **Ms 5153** (bap entries apparently identical to those in Ms 5152; mar entries in abbreviated form; some bur entries record fees paid). Rough mar 1695-1702, **in Ms 5144** (incomplete). Mar from 1701 entered in greater detail **in Ms 5145**; see St Michael Paternoster Royal. Indexes to Ms 5152: **Boyd** (mar); T.C. Dale, 'Index to the marriage registers of ... St Michael Paternoster Royal and St Martin Vintry ...' (typescript, also microfilm copy; 1932), **GL Printed Books Section**.

Bap and bur 1722-1812, **Ms 5154**. Includes entries for 1719/20-22, duplicates of those in Ms 5152 above.

Bap 1813-1906, **Ms 5155**. Index: **in Webb 1** (1813-40).

Mar 1701-1812: see St Michael Paternoster Royal.

Mar 1813-36, **Ms 5156**. Index: Dale, as above, **GL Printed Books Section**.

Bur 1813-49, **Ms 5157**. Index: **in Webb 54/1-2**.

For later reg (bap from c.1906, mar from 1837, banns from 1754), and for mar licences from 1809, see St Michael Paternoster Royal.

Transcripts:

Bap, mar and bur 1617-49, **Ms 5158**.

Mar 1617-49 and 1675-1710, **Challen 9**.

Bap, mar and bur 1629-30/1 and 1639-39/40 (from b tr), **Webb 4**. Indexed.

Bap 1813-40, **Webb 1**. Indexed.

B tr of bap, mar and bur 1629-30/1, **in Ms 10107**; bap, mar and bur 1639-39/40, **in Ms 10107A**; bap 1800-1, 1804 and 1807-39, mar 1800-1, 1804 and 1807-12 (from reg of St Michael Paternoster Royal with St Martin Vintry), mar 1813-36, bur 1800-1, 1804 and 1807-39, **Ms 11234**; bap 1840-54, bur 1840-9, **Ms 9314**.

ST MARY ABCHURCH

Partial index to bap and mar in **IGI**.

Bap, mar and bur 1558-1736/7 (mar with St Lawrence Pountney from c.1670), **Ms 7666**. Index: **Boyd** (mar).

Bap, mar and bur 1737-1812, banns 1757-62 (mar and banns with St Lawrence Pountney), **in Ms 7667**.

Note: Ms 7667 contains five sections, in the following order:
St Mary with St Lawrence mar 1737-54
St Mary bap 1737-1812
St Mary bur 1737-1812
St Lawrence bap and bur 1740-1812
St Mary with St Lawrence mar 1754-1812 and banns 1757-62.

Index: **Boyd** (mar to 1775 and from 1801, banns 1757-62).

Bap 1813-1978 (with St Lawrence Pountney from c.1907), bur 1813-51, **in Ms 24742**.

Note: Ms 24742 contains four sections, in the following order:
St Mary (with St Lawrence from c.1907) bap 1813-1978
St Mary bur 1813-51
St Lawrence bap 1813-1907
St Lawrence bur 1813-50.

Index: **in Webb 54/1-2** (bur).

Mar 1813-37 (with St Lawrence Pountney; entered in separate series), **Ms 7668**. Indexes: in reg (St Lawrence Pountney males only); **Boyd**.

Mar 1837-1953 (with St Lawrence Pountney), **Ms 24743**.

Banns 1804-1911 (with St Lawrence Pountney), **Ms 7669/1**.

Banns 1911-53 (with St Lawrence Pountney), **Ms 7669/2**.

Transcripts:

Mar 1558-1736/7, **Challen 5**.

Mar 1737-1812 (with St Lawrence Pountney) and 1813-37, banns 1757-62 (with St Lawrence Pountney), **Challen 13** .

B tr of bap, mar and bur 1802 (May)-1803 (Jul.), 1803 (Apr.)-1804 (Apr.), 1805 (Nov.)-1806 (Nov.), 1807-21 and 1823, **Ms 10423A**.

ST MARY ALDERMANBURY

United to St Alphage London Wall, 1917; St Giles Cripplegate, 1954

Partial index to bap and mar in **IGI**.

Bap 1538-1722, mar 1538-1721, bur 1538-1722, **Ms 3572/1**. Indexes: **Boyd** (mar 1701-21); **in HS 61-2** (bap, mar and bur).

Bap 1722-1812, mar 1722-54, bur 1722-1812, **Ms 3572/2**. Indexes: **Boyd** (mar from 1751); **in HS 65** (bap, mar and bur).

Bap 1813-1940, bur 1813-59, **in Ms 3572/3**. Rough bap 1813-61 and bur 1813-56, **Ms 3577** (some entries omitted; others apparently identical to those in Ms 3572/3). Indexes to Ms 3572/3: **in HS 65** (bap to 1837 and bur to 1859); **in Webb 3** (bap 1838-1940 of persons born before 1841); **in Webb 54/1-2** (bur).

Mar 1754-91, banns 1754-1804, **Ms 3573**. Indexes: **Boyd** (mar to 1775); **in HS 65** (mar).

Mar 1791-1812, **Ms 3574/1**. Indexes: **Boyd** (from 1801); **in HS 65**.

Mar 1813-37, **in Ms 3572/3**. Indexes: **Boyd**; **in HS 65**.

Mar 1837-1940, **Ms 3574/2**.

Banns 1804-54, **Ms 3575**.

Banns 1852-1940, **Ms 3576.**

Mar licences collection 1837-1928, **Ms 3593**.

Transcripts:

Bap 1538-1722, mar 1538-1721, bur 1538-1722, **HS 61-2**. Indexed.

Bap and mar 1722-1837, bur 1722-1859, **HS 65**. Indexed.

B tr of bap, mar and bur 1800-2, 1804 and 1807-12, **Ms 10441**; 1813-36, **Ms 10441A**.

ST MARY ALDERMARY

Partial index to bap and mar in **IGI**.

Bap, mar and bur 1558-1653, **Ms 8990/1**. Indexes: **Boyd** (mar); **in HS 5** (bap, mar and bur).

Bap 1653-1721/2, mar 1653-1728/9 and 1736-43 (with St Thomas Apostle from 1672), bur 1653-1728/9, **Ms 8990/2**. Indexes: **Boyd** (mar); **in HS 5** (bap, mar and bur).

Bap 1722-1812, mar 1729-36 and 1744-54 (with St Thomas Apostle), bur 1729-1812, **Ms 8991**. One mar 1744, **in Ms 9009**. Indexes: **Boyd** (mar); **in HS 5** (bap, mar and bur to 1754); **in Webb 8** (bap and bur from 1754).

Bap 1813-1910 (with St Thomas Apostle, St Antholin Budge Row and St John the Baptist Walbrook from 1873), **Ms 8994**. Index: **in Webb 8** (to 1840).

Mar 1754-75, banns 1754-70, **Ms 8992**. Index: **in Webb 8**.

Mar 1776-1812, **in Ms 8993**. Index: **in Webb 8**.

Mar 1813-36, **Ms 8995**. Index: **in Webb 8**.

Mar 1837-1940 (with St Thomas Apostle, St Antholin Budge Row and St John the Baptist Walbrook from 1873), **Ms 8995A**.

Banns 1771-1873, **Ms 8997**.

Banns 1874-1952 (with St Thomas Apostle, St Antholin Budge Row and St John the Baptist Walbrook), **in Ms 8998**.

Mar licences collection 1860-1909 (with St Thomas Apostle from 1860, and with St Antholin Budge Row and St John the Baptist Walbrook from 1874), **Ms 9049**.

Bur 1813-51, **Ms 8996**. Bur accounts 1813-38, **in Ms 4866** (recording causes of death). Index to Ms 8996: **in Webb 8 and 54/1-2**.

Later bap and mar reg retained by incumbent.

Transcripts:

Bap, mar and bur 1558-1754, **HS 5**. Indexed.

Bap 1754-1840, bap 1841-1910 of persons born before 1841, mar 1754-1837, bur 1754-1851, **Webb 8**. Indexed.

B tr of bap, 1813-50, mar 1813-36, bur 1813-50, **Ms 11235**. Note: b tr of bap, mar and bur 1799-1813 are held by Lambeth Palace Library, London SE1 7JU.

ST MARY AT HILL

Partial index to bap and mar in **IGI**.

Bap 1558-1812, mar 1558/9-1754, bur 1558-1812 (bap and bur with St Andrew Hubbard 1742-1812), **Ms 4546**. Index: **Boyd** (mar 1701-54).

Bap 1813-65, **Ms 23810**. Rough bap 1822-5 and bur 1796-1825 (with St Andrew Hubbard), **Ms 23811**.

Bap 1865-1988 (with St Andrew Hubbard 1813-1988, also with St Botolph Billingsgate and St George Botolph Lane from 1891), **Ms 29098**.

Mar 1754-84, banns 1754-1813 (both with St Andrew Hubbard), **Ms 4547/1**. One mar 1783 (Sep.) **in Ms 4547/2**. Index: **in Webb 102** (mar).

Mar 1784-1812 (with St Andrew Hubbard), **Ms 4547/2**. Index: **in Webb 102**.

Mar 1813-37, **Ms 4548**. Index: **in Webb 102**.

Later mar reg retained by incumbent. B tr of mar 1846, **in Ms 10431A**.

Banns 1824-1921 (with St Andrew Hubbard, also, from c.1890, with St Botolph Billingsgate and St George Botolph Lane), **Ms 23812**.

Bur 1813-50, **Ms 4549**. Index: **in Webb 54/1-2**.

Transcripts:

Mar 1558/9-1754, **Challen 27**.

Mar 1754-1837, **in Webb 102**. Indexed.

B tr of bap, mar and bur 1800-12, **Ms 10431**; bap 1813-44 and 1846, mar 1813-37 and 1846, bur 1813-44 and 1846 (all with St Andrew Hubbard), **Ms 10431A**.

ST MARY AXE

United to St Andrew Undershaft, 1560/1

No reg for this parish are known; it would appear that early registrations are included in the reg of St Andrew Undershaft, *q.v.*

ST MARY BOTHAW

United to St Swithin London Stone, 1670; St Stephen Walbrook, 1954

Partial index to bap in **IGI**.

Bap 1536-1653/4, mar 1536-1657/8, bur 1536/7-1653, **Ms 4310**.

Mar 1754-1812, banns 1754-64, **Ms 4316**. Index: **Boyd** (except 1776-1800).

For bap 1675-1944, mar 1672-1754 and 1813-1941, banns 1778-1852, bur c.1670-1853, see St Swithin London Stone.

Transcripts:

Mar 1536-1657/8 and 1754-1812, banns 1754-64, **Challen 31**.

Note: b tr of bap, mar and bur 1799-1802, 1804 and 1808-11 are held by Lambeth Palace Library, London SE1 7JU.

ST MARY COLECHURCH

United to St Mildred Poultry, 1670; St Olave Jewry, 1871; St Margaret Lothbury, 1886

Partial index to bap in **IGI**.

Bap 1558-1670, mar 1558-1665/6, bur 1558-1666, **Ms 4438**. Includes mar 1592 and 1683/4-84 and bur 1563-1666 at Mercers' Hall Chapel. Index: **Boyd** (mar).

Bap and bur 1671-1812, **Ms 4439**. Includes bur 1671-1715 at Mercers' Hall Chapel.

For later reg and for mar licences collection from 1810 see St Mildred Poultry.

Transcripts:

Mar 1558-1665/6 and 1683/4-84, **Challen 8**.

B tr of bap, mar and bur 1630-30/1, **in Ms 10107**; bap, mar and bur 1665-65/6, **in Ms 10952**; bap and bur 1800, 1802-4 and 1807-10, **Ms 10439**. For later b tr see St Mildred Poultry.

ST MARY LE BOW

Partial index to bap and mar in **IGI**.

Bap, mar and bur 1538-1631, **Ms 4996**. Indexes: **Boyd** (mar); **in HS 45** (bap, mar and bur).

Bap 1631-53, mar 1631-75, bur 1631-53: no reg extant.

Bap 1653-97, mar 1675-97 (with Allhallows Honey Lane and St Pancras Soper Lane), bur 1653-97, **in Ms 4997**. Indexes: **Boyd** (mar); **in HS 45** (bap, mar and bur).

Bap 1697/8-1771, mar 1697/8-1754, bur 1697/8-1769 (all with Allhallows Honey Lane and St Pancras Soper Lane), **Ms 4998**. Indexes: **Boyd** (mar); **in HS 45** (bap, mar and bur).

Bap 1771-1812, bur 1769-1812 (both with Allhallows Honey Lane and St Pancras Soper Lane), **Ms 5000**. Index: **in HS 45**.

Bap 1814-1992 (with St Pancras Soper Lane from 1889 and with Allhallows Honey Lane, Allhallows Bread Street and St John the Evangelist Friday Street from 1892), **Ms 21727**. Index (to 1837): **in HS 45**.

Mar 1754-95, banns 1754-1831 (both with Allhallows Honey Lane and St Pancras Soper Lane), **Ms 4999**. Indexes: **Boyd**; **in HS 45**.

Mar 1795-1812 (with Allhallows Honey Lane and St Pancras Soper Lane), **Ms 5003**. Indexes: **Boyd**; **in HS 45**.

Mar 1813-34, **Ms 5001/1**. Indexes: **Boyd**; **in HS 45**.

Mar 1835-7, **Ms 5001/2**. Indexes: **Boyd**; **in HS 45**.

Mar 1837-1992 (with Allhallows Honey Lane and St Pancras Soper Lane from 1837 and with Allhallows Bread Street and St John the Evangelist Friday Street from 1876), **Ms 5001/3**.

Banns 1831-1937 (with Allhallows Honey Lane and St Pancras Soper Lane from 1831, and with Allhallows Bread Street and St John the Evangelist Friday Street from c.1876), **Ms 5002**. Indexes (to 1837): **Boyd**; **in HS 45**.

Bur 1813-52, **Ms 5004**. Indexes: **in HS 44-5**; **in Webb 54/1-2**.

Transcripts:

Bap 1538-1631 and 1653-1837, bur 1538-1631 and 1653-1852, **HS 44**. Indexed **in HS 45**.

Mar 1538-1631 and 1675-1837, banns 1754-1837, **HS 45**. Indexed.

B tr of bap 1817-46, 1848-56, 1858-62 and 1867, mar 1817-38, bur 1817-46 and 1848-52, in **Ms 14565**. Note: b tr of bap, mar and bur 1799-1808 and 1812 are held by Lambeth Palace Library, London SE1 7JU.

ST MARY MAGDALEN MILK STREET

United to St Lawrence Jewry, 1670

Partial index to bap and mar in **IGI**.

Receipts for bur (with names of deceased) 1518-1606, in churchwardens' accounts, **in Ms 2596/1**.

Bap 1558-1653, mar 1559-1659/60, bur 1558-1653, **in Ms 6984**. Indexes: **Boyd** (mar); **in HS 72** (bap, mar and bur); **in Ms 3292** (bap, mar and bur).

Bap 1653-77, mar 1653-66, bur 1653-65, **Ms 6985**. Indexes: **Boyd** (mar); **in HS 72** (bap, mar and bur); **in Ms 3292** (bap, mar and bur).

For later reg see St Lawrence Jewry.

Transcripts:

Bap 1558-1667, mar 1559-1666, bur 1558-1665, **HS 72**. Indexed.

Mar 1559-1666, **Challen 9**.

B tr of bap, mar and bur 1639-40, **in Ms 10107A**.

ST MARY MAGDALEN OLD FISH STREET
United to St Martin Ludgate, 1890

Partial index to bap and mar in **IGI**.

Bap 1539-1645, mar 1539-1638/9, bur 1539-1643, **Ms 11529**. Index: **in Webb 40** (mar).

Bap 1645-64, mar 1639-64, bur 1643-64: no reg extant.

Bap 1664/5-1717, mar 1664/5-1712, bur 1664/5-1717, **Ms 10221**. Index: **Boyd** (mar).

Mar 1712-18, **Ms 10222**. Index: **Boyd**.

Bap 1717-33, mar 1718-32, bur 1717-32, **Ms 10223**. Index: **Boyd** (mar).

Bap 1733-57, mar 1733-54, bur 1733-50, **Ms 10224**. Index: **Boyd** (mar).

Bap 1757-1812, bur 1751-1812, **Ms 10225**.

Bap 1813-92 (with St Gregory by St Paul from 1882), **Ms 10226**.

Mar 1754-1812, banns 1755-70, **Ms 10227**. Index: **in Webb 40**.

Mar 1813-37, **Ms 10228**. Index: **in Webb 40**.

Mar 1837-86 (with St Gregory by St Paul from 1868), **Ms 10229**.

Banns 1790-1877 (with St Gregory by St Paul), **Ms 18939**.

Banns 1877-1958 (with St Gregory by St Paul and, from 1890, with St Martin Ludgate), **Ms 23904**.

Mar licences collection 1687-1834 (with St Gregory by St Paul), held by the Archivist, College of Arms, Queen Victoria Street, London EC4V 4BT (available by appointment only).

Bur 1813-53, **Ms 10230**. Index: **in Webb 54/1-2**.

For later bap and mar see St Martin Ludgate.

Transcripts:

Mar 1539-1638/9 and 1754-1837, banns 1755-70, **Webb 40**. Indexed.

Mar 1664/5-1754, **Challen 10**.

B tr of bap, mar and bur 1800-12, **Ms 10426**; 1813-21, **Ms 10426A**.

ST MARY MOUNTHAW

United to St Mary Somerset, 1670; St Nicholas Cole Abbey, 1866

Partial index to bap and mar in **IGI**.

Bap 1568-1711, mar 1568-1666, bur 1568-1711, **Ms 5703**. Indexes: **Boyd** (mar); **in HS 58** (bap, mar and bur).

Bap and bur 1711-1812, **Ms 5704**. Rough bap and bur from 1769**, in Ms 5708A** (recording, besides details in Ms 5704, fees paid; some bap entries record dates of birth, some bur entries record ages of deceased and causes of death). Index to Ms 5704: **in HS 58**.

Bap 1813-87, **Ms 5706**. Rough bap to 1819, **in Ms 5708A** (recording, besides details in Ms 5706, fees paid; some entries record dates of birth). Indexes to Ms 5706: **in HS 58** (to 1837); **in Webb 3** (bap 1838-87 of persons born before 1841).

For later bap see St Nicholas Cole Abbey.

Mar c.1671-1754: see St Mary Somerset.

Mar 1754-1809, **Ms 5705**. Indexes: **Boyd** (except 1776-1800); **in HS 58**.

Mar 1814-35, **Ms 5707/1**. Indexes: **Boyd**; **in HS 58**.

Mar 1837-49, **Ms 5707/2**.

For later mar see St Mary Somerset.

Bur 1813-49, **Ms 5708**. Rough bur to 1819, **in Ms 5708A** (recording, besides details in Ms 5708, fees paid; some entries record causes of death). Indexes to Ms 5708: **in HS 58**; **in Webb 54/1-2**.

Transcripts:

Bap 1568-1837, mar 1568-1666, 1754-1809 and 1814-35, bur 1568-1849, **HS 58**. Indexed.

B tr of bap 1800-4 and 1807-19, mar 1800-1, 1803-4, 1807-9 and 1814-19, bur 1800-4 and 1807-19, **Ms 11339**. For later b tr see St Mary Somerset.

ST MARY SOMERSET

United to St Nicholas Cole Abbey, 1866

Partial index to bap and mar in **IGI**.

Bap and mar 1558/9-1653, bur 1557/8-1654, **Ms 5710/1**. Indexes: **Boyd** (mar); **in HS 59** (bap and mar); **in HS 60** (bur).

Births 1653-8, bap 1658-1711, mar 1653-1709 (with St Mary Mounthaw from c.1671), bur 1653-1711, **Ms 5710/2**. Indexes: **Boyd** (mar); **in HS 59** (births, bap and mar); **in HS 60** (bur).

Note: bur 1653 (Oct.)-1654 (Jun.) are duplicates of the entries for these dates in Ms 5710/1.

Bap 1711-74, mar 1711-54 (with St Mary Mounthaw), bur 1711-74, **Ms 5710/3** (also contains tr of mar 1754-5, from Ms 5712/1). Rough bap and bur from 1769, **in Ms 5708A** (recording, besides details in Ms 5710/3, fees paid; some bap entries record dates of birth). Indexes to Ms 5710/3: **Boyd** (mar); **in HS 59** (bap and mar); **in HS 60** (bur).

Bap 1775-1812, **Ms 5711/1**. Rough bap for these dates, **in Ms 5708A** (recording, besides details in Ms 5711/1, fees paid; some entries record dates of birth). Index to Ms 5711/1: **in HS 59**.

Bap 1813-80, **Ms 5711/2**. Rough bap to 1819, **in Ms 5708A** (recording, besides details in Ms 5711/2, fees paid; some entries record dates of birth). Indexes to Ms 5711/2: **in HS 59** (to 1837); **in Webb 3** (bap 1838-80 of persons born before 1841).

Mar 1754-89, banns 1754-8**, Ms 5712/1**. Indexes: **Boyd** (mar to 1775); **in HS 59** (mar and banns).

Mar 1789-1812, **Ms 5712/2**. Indexes: **Boyd** (from 1801); **in HS 59**.

Mar 1813-37, **Ms 5712/3**. Indexes: **Boyd**; **in HS 59**.

Mar 1837-78 (with St Mary Mounthaw from 1851), **Ms 5712/4**.

For banns 1877-89 (with St Mary Mounthaw) see St Nicholas Cole Abbey.

Bur 1775-1812, **Ms 5713/1**. Rough bur for these dates, **in Ms 5708A** (recording, besides details in Ms 5713/1, fees paid; some entries record ages of deceased and causes of death). Index to Ms 5713/1: **in HS 60**.

Bur 1813-53, **Ms 5713/2**. Rough bur to 1819, **in Ms 5708A** (recording, besides details in Ms 5713/2, fees paid; some entries record causes of death). Indexes to Ms 5713/2: **in HS 60**; **in Webb 54/1-2**.

For later bap and mar see St Nicholas Cole Abbey.

Transcripts:

Bap and mar 1558/9-1837, **HS 59**. Indexed.

Bur 1557/8-1853, **HS 60**. Indexed.

B tr of bap, mar and bur 1800-5 and 1807-19, **Ms 10425**; 1820-9 and 1831-2 (with St Mary Mounthaw from 1820), **Ms 10425A**.

ST MARY STAINING

United to St Michael Wood Street, 1670; St Alban Wood Street, 1894; St Vedast Foster Lane, 1954

Partial index to bap in **IGI**.

Bap 1673-1812, **Ms 6533**. Index: **in Webb 106**.

Mar from 1754: see St Michael Wood Street.

Bur 1678-1812: see St Michael Wood Street.

All other reg of this parish were destroyed either in the Great Fire or by enemy action in 1940. The following sources are available:

> B tr of bap, mar and bur 1629-31, **in Ms 10107**. Index: **in Webb 106**.
>
> B tr of bap 1813-20 (with St Michael Wood Street), **in Ms 10416**. Index: **in Webb 106**.
>
> Receipts for bur (with names of deceased) in churchwardens' accounts, 1644-78, **in Ms 1542/2**; 1813-36, **in Ms 1542/5**.
>
> B tr of bur 1813-20 (with St Michael Wood Street), **in Ms 10416**. Index: **in Webb 106**.

Transcripts:

Bap, mar and bur 1629-31 (from b tr), bap 1673-1812 (from reg) and bur 1805 and 1807-12 (from b tr), **Webb 12**. Index: **in Webb 106**. For transcript and index of bur 1678-1812 (from reg), see St Michael Wood Street.

B tr of bap, mar and bur 1629-31, **in Ms 10107**; 1800-20*, **Ms 10416**.

* St Michael Wood Street with St Mary Staining, except:- 1804, St Michael Wood Street only; 1812, St Mary Staining only.

ST MARY WOOLCHURCH HAW

United to St Mary Woolnoth, 1670

Partial index to bap and mar in **IGI**.

Bap 1558-1693/4, mar 1559-1666, bur 1558-1665/6, **Ms 7644**. Indexes: **Boyd** (mar); in J.M.S. Brooke and A.W.C. Hallen, *Transcript of the Registers ... of St Mary Woolnoth and St Mary Woolchurch Haw ...* (London, 1886), **GL Printed Books Section** (bap, mar and bur).

Bap 1693/4-1814, mar c.1670-1812, banns 1754-1823, bur c.1670-1812: for main series of registrations, see St Mary Woolnoth. One bap 1699, **in Ms 7644**.

Bap 1814-89, **Ms 7645**. Includes tr of bap 1813-14 from Ms 7639A. Index: **in Webb 5**.

For later bap see St Mary Woolnoth.

Mar 1814-37, **Ms 7646**. Index: **in Webb 5**.

Banns 1824-65, **Ms 8102**.

For later mar and banns see St Mary Woolnoth.

Bur 1813-48, **in Ms 7647**. Index: **in Webb 5 and 54/1-2**.

Transcripts:

Bap 1558-1693/4 and 1699, mar 1559-1666, bur 1558-1665/6, Brooke and Hallen, as above, **GL Printed Books Section**. Indexed.

Bap 1813-89, mar 1814-37, bur 1813-48, **Webb 5**. Indexed.

B tr of bap, mar and bur 1629-30/1, **in Ms 10107**; 1639-39/40, **in Ms 10107A**; 1801-12 (from reg of St Mary Woolnoth with St Mary Woolchurch Haw), **Ms 10437**; 1813-30, **Ms 10437A**. For later b tr see St Mary Woolnoth.

ST MARY WOOLNOTH

Partial index to bap and mar in **IGI**.

Bap, mar and bur 1538-1641, **Ms 7635/1**. Indexes: **Boyd** (mar); in J.M.S. Brooke and A.W.C. Hallen, *Transcript of the registers ... of St Mary Woolnoth and St Mary Woolchurch Haw ...* (London, 1886), **GL Printed Books Section** (bap, mar and bur).

Bap 1641-93, mar 1641-1715, bur 1641-86 (mar and bur with St Mary Woolchurch Haw from c.1670), **Ms 7635/2**. Rough mar 1695-1706, **in Ms 7637** (with some variant entries). Indexes to Ms 7635/2: **Boyd** (mar); in Brooke and Hallen, as above, **GL Printed Books Section** (bap, mar and bur).

Bap 1693/4-1727, bur 1686-1722 (both with St Mary Woolchurch Haw), **Ms 7636**. Rough bap and bur 1695-1706, **in Ms 7637** (with some variant entries). Index to Ms 7636: in Brooke and Hallen, as above, **GL Printed Books Section**.

No mar solemnised 1716-26 during rebuilding of church.

Bap 1727-44, mar 1727-32 (both with St Mary Woolchurch Haw), **Ms 7638**. Two mar 1727, **in Ms 7635/2** (duplicates of entries in Ms 7638). Indexes: **Boyd** (mar); in Brooke and Hallen, as above, **GL Printed Books Section** (bap and mar).

Mar 1732-44, bur 1722-44: reg not extant. Receipts for bur (with names of deceased) for these dates, in churchwardens' accounts, **in Ms 1002/2**. List of coffins dated 1726-44, removed from the church in 1892-3 and re-interred at the City of London cemetery, Little Ilford, **in Ms 7643** (p 50). Duplicate of this list, **in Ms 7647**.

Bap 1744-1806, mar 1745-54, bur 1744-1806 (all with St Mary Woolchurch Haw), **Ms 7639**. Indexes: **Boyd** (mar); in Brooke and Hallen, as above, **GL Printed Books Section** (bap to 1760, mar to 1754, bur to 1760); **in Webb 5** (bap and bur from 1761).

> Note: list of coffins "particulars of which cannot be found in the parish registers" dated 1758-1830, removed from the church in 1892-3 and re-interred at the City of London cemetery, Little Ilford, **in Ms 7643** (pp 50-1). Duplicate of this list, **in Ms 7647**.

Bap 1807-14, bur 1807-12 (both with St Mary Woolchurch Haw), **Ms 7639A**. Index: **in Webb 5**.

Bap 1814-1985 (with St Mary Woolchurch Haw from c.1889), **Ms 21549**. Includes tr of bap in 1813 from Ms 7639A. Index: **in Webb 5** (1813-30, from b tr); **in Webb 102** (1831-40).

Mar 1754-1800, banns 1754-67 and 1782-1800 (all with St Mary Woolchurch Haw), **Ms 7640/1**. Rough banns 1759-90, **Ms 8100/1**, and from 1791, **in Ms 8100/2**. Index to mar: **in Webb 5**.

Mar 1801-13, banns 1801-23 (both with St Mary Woolchurch Haw), **Ms 7640/2**. Rough banns to 1823, **in Ms 8100/2**. Index to mar: **in Webb 5**.

Mar 1813-37, **Ms 7641**. Index: **in Webb 5**.

Mar 1837-1953 (with St Mary Woolchurch Haw), **Ms 7642**, 4 vol.
1. 1837-1914 2. 1914-35 3. 1935-53 4. 1953.

Banns 1824-59, **Ms 8101**.

Banns 1861-1951 (with St Mary Woolchurch Haw), **Ms 7642A**.

Bur 1813-52, **in Ms 7643**. Includes list of coffins "particulars of which cannot be found in the parish registers" dated 1758-1830, removed from the church in 1892-3 and re-interred at the City of London cemetery, Little Ilford. Index: **in Webb 5 and 54/1-2**.

Transcripts:

Bap 1538-1760, mar 1538-1715, 1727-32 and 1745-54, bur 1538-1722 and 1744-60, Brooke and Hallen, as above, **GL Printed Books Section**. Indexed.

Bap 1761-1830, mar 1754-1837, bur 1761-1852, **Webb 5**. Indexed.

Bap 1831-40, **in Webb 102**. Indexed.

B tr of bap, mar and bur 1629-29/30, **in Ms 10107**; bap, mar and bur 1639-39/40, **in Ms 10107A**; bap, mar and bur 1665-6, **in Ms 10952**; bap, mar and bur 1801-12, **Ms 10436**; bap, mar and bur 1813-30, **Ms 10436A**; bap and bur 1840-1 (with St Mary Woolchurch Haw), **Ms 10436B**; bur 1842, **Ms 18516**.

ST MATTHEW FRIDAY STREET

United to St Vedast Foster Lane, 1882

Partial index to bap and mar in **IGI**.

Bap, mar and bur 1538-1812 (mar with St Peter Westcheap from c.1699): reg destroyed by enemy action in 1940. Tr **in HS 63** (indexed); mar also transcribed **in Challen 12**, and indexed (except 1776-1800) in **Boyd**. B tr (St Matthew only) of bap, mar and bur 1665-65/6, **in Ms 10952**; 1800 (Jan.)-1802 (Apr.), 1803 (May)-1804 (May), 1805 (Dec.)-1809 (Jan.) and 1809 (Dec.)-1811 (Dec.), **Ms 11162**.

Bap 1813-82, **Ms 6497** (now incomplete following damage by enemy action in 1940). B tr of bap 1813-44 and 1848-55, **in Ms 10451**. The reg and b tr entries 1813-40 are transcribed, collated and indexed **in Webb 2**.

For later bap see St Vedast Foster Lane.

Mar 1814-36, **Ms 6498**. Index: **Boyd**.

Mar 1837-89 (with St Peter Westcheap): reg destroyed by enemy action in 1940. Duplicate reg deposited at the London City Register Office, Finsbury Town Hall, Rosebery Avenue, London ECIR 4QT.

Later mar were entered in reg of St Vedast Foster Lane; these were damaged beyond repair by enemy action in 1940, and are not available for use.

Bur 1813-46, **Ms 6499**. Index: **in Webb 2 and 54/1-2**.

Transcripts:

Bap, mar and bur 1538-1812, **HS 63**. Indexed.

Mar 1538-1836, **Challen 12**.

Bap 1813-40, bap 1841-82 of persons born before 1841, bur 1813-46, **Webb 2**. Indexed.

Bap 1857-82, **in Ms 10955**.

B tr of bap, mar and bur 1665-65/6, **in Ms 10952**; bap, mar and bur 1800 (Jan.)-1802 (Apr.), 1803 (May)-1804 (May), 1805 (Dec.)-1809 (Jan.) and 1809 (Dec.)-1811 (Dec.), **Ms 11162**; bap 1813-44 and 1848-55, mar 1814-36, bur 1813-44, **in Ms 10451**.

ST MICHAEL BASSISHAW

United to St Lawrence Jewry, 1897

Partial index to bap and mar in **IGI**.

Bap 1538-1661/2, mar 1538-1665, bur 1538-1662, **Ms 6986**. Parchment copy (compiled from 1600) of bap 1557-1663, mar 1557-1661, bur 1557-1663/4, **Ms 6987** (with some variant entries). These two vol are transcribed, collated and indexed **in HS 72-3**; mar also indexed in **Boyd**.

Bap 1661/2-1733, mar 1671/2-1733, bur 1662-1735, **Ms 6988/1**. Bap to 1663 and bur to 1663/4, also **in Ms 6987**. Indexes: **Boyd** (mar); **in HS 73** (bap, mar and bur).

Bap 1733-1812, mar 1733-64, bur 1735-1812, **Ms 6988/2**. Indexes: **Boyd** (mar); **in HS 74** (bap, mar and bur).

Bap 1813-92, **Ms 6989**. Index: **in HS 74**.

Bap c.1897-1940: entered in reg of St Lawrence Jewry and damaged beyond repair by enemy action in 1940.

For later bap see St Lawrence Jewry.

Mar 1764-1837, **Ms 6990/1**. Indexes: in reg; **in HS 74**.

Mar 1837-90, **Ms 6990/2**.

Banns 1755-99, **Ms 2489**.

Banns 1800-92, **Ms 6991**.

For later mar and banns see St Lawrence Jewry.

Mar licences collection 1841-90, **Ms 2508**.

Bur 1813-53, **Ms 6992**. Indexes: **in HS 74**; **in Webb 54/1-2**.

Transcripts:

Bap 1538-1892, mar 1538-1837, bur 1538-1853, **HS 72-4**. Indexed.

Mar 1538-1764, **Challen 9**.

B tr of bap, mar and bur 1629-30/1, **in Ms 10107**; bap 1800-3, 1807-22 (May), 1834-45 and 1847-8, mar 1800-3, 1807-21 and 1834-6, bur 1800-3, 1807-21, 1834-45 and 1847-8, **Ms 11237**.

ST MICHAEL CORNHILL

Partial index to bap and mar in **IGI**.

Receipts for bur (with names of deceased) 1455-75 and 1547-59, in churchwardens' accounts, **in Ms 4071/1**. Transcribed in W.H. Overall, *The accounts of the churchwardens of St Michael Cornhill ...* (London, 1871), **GL Printed Books Section**.

Bap and mar 1546-1735/6, banns 1653-59/60, bur 1546-1736, entered in three vol, **Ms 4061**, **Ms 4062** and **Ms 4063/1**, as follows:

Bap, mar and bur 1546-98, **in Ms 4061**. Parchment copy 1558-98, **in Ms 4062.**

Bap 1598-1654, mar and bur 1598-1653, **in Ms 4062**. Rough bap, mar and bur for these dates, **in Ms 4061** (some entries omit details found in Ms 4062). Dates of birth from 1653, **in Ms 4063/1**.

Bap 1654-7, **in Ms 4061**. Dates of birth to 1657, **in Ms 4063/1**.

Bap 1657/8-1735/6, mar 1653/4-1735/6, banns 1653-59/60, bur 1653-1736, **in Ms 4063/1**. Rough mar 1653/4-57, **in Ms 4061** (including some additional mar not found in Ms 4063/1, but omitting other entries recorded there). Duplicate of rough mar 1653/4-54, **in Ms 4062**. Rough bur 1653 (Oct.), **in Ms 4061**. Rough bap, mar and bur from 1702, **in Ms 4064** (most entries in abbreviated form).

These reg are transcribed, collated and indexed **in HS 7**; mar also indexed in **Boyd** (except 1651-1700).

Bap 1735/6-83, mar 1736-54, bur 1736-83, **Ms 4063/2**. Rough bap, mar and bur to 1750/1, **in Ms 4064** (some entries in abbreviated form). Indexes: **Boyd** (mar); **in HS 7** (bap, mar and bur to 1754); **in Webb 10** (bap and bur from 1754).

Mar 1754-83, banns 1754-87, **Ms 4065**. Indexes: **Boyd** (to 1775); **in Webb 10**.

Bap, mar and bur 1783-1803, **Ms 4066/1**. Indexes: **Boyd** (mar from 1801); **in Webb 10** (bap, mar and bur).

Bap, mar and bur 1803-12, **Ms 4066/2**. Indexes: **Boyd** (mar); **in Webb 10** (bap, mar and bur).

Bap 1813-1986 (with St Peter le Poer and St Benet Fink from 1906), **Ms 21733**. Tr and index of bap 1813-40, and bap 1841-70 of persons born before 1841, **in Webb 10** (from b tr).

Mar 1813-36, **Ms 4067**. Indexes: **Boyd**; **in Webb 10**.

Mar 1837-1970 (with St Peter le Poer and St Benet Fink from c.1904), **Ms 31599**.

Banns 1853-1931, **Ms 22502**.

Bur 1813-53, **Ms 4068**. Index: **in Webb 10 and 54/1-2**.

Transcripts:

Bap, mar and bur 1546-1754, **HS 7**. Indexed.

Bap 1754-1840, bap 1841-70 of persons born before 1841, mar 1754-1836, banns 1754-87, bur 1754-1853, **Webb 10**. Indexed.

B tr of bap, mar and bur 1629-30/1, **in Ms 10107**; bap, mar and bur 1800-4 and 1806-12, **Ms 10434**; bap 1813-60, 1862-3 and 1865-87, mar 1813-36, bur 1813-53, **Ms 14566**.

ST MICHAEL CROOKED LANE

United to St Magnus the Martyr, 1831

Partial index to bap and mar in **IGI**.

Bap 1538/9-1723, mar 1539-1723, bur 1538-1723, **Ms 11367**. Indexes: **Boyd** (mar); also **in Ms 11374**, 7 vol, for which see list below.

Bap 1723-1812, mar 1723-54, bur 1723-1812, **Ms 11368**. Indexes: **Boyd** (mar); also **in Ms 11374**, 7 vol, and **in Ms 11366**, 3 vol, for which see lists below.

Bap 1813-90, **Ms 11369**. Index: **in Ms 11366/8**.

Later bap entered in reg of St Magnus the Martyr.

Mar and banns 1754-79, **Ms 11370/1**. Indexes: **Boyd** (to 1775); **in Ms 11374/5** (mar).

Mar 1779-1812, banns 1779-1823, **Ms 11370/2**. Indexes: **Boyd** (from 1801); **in Ms 11374/5** (mar to 1799); **in Ms 11366/9** (mar from 1800).

Mar 1813-35, **Ms 11370/3**. Indexes: Boyd; in **Ms 11366/9**.

For mar from 1838 see St Magnus the Martyr.

Banns 1824-1949 (with St Magnus the Martyr and St Margaret New Fish Street from 1840), **Ms 11371**. Some banns c.1840-1952, omitted from Ms 11371, entered **in Ms 11364**. Index to banns to 1835: **Boyd**.

Mar licences collection 1754-1830, **Ms 21750**. Index: **in Ms 24657**.

For later mar licences see St Magnus the Martyr.

Bur 1813-52, **Ms 11372**. Bur 1816-18 also **in Ms 11373** (recording places of interment). Indexes to Ms 11372: **in Ms 11366/10**; **in Webb 54/1-2**.

Transcripts:

Mar 1539-1779, banns 1754-79, **Challen 7**.

Mar and banns 1779-1835, **Challen 22**.

B tr of bap 1813-42, 1844, 1846-8 and 1850, mar 1813-35, bur 1813-42, 1844, 1846 and 1848, **Ms 11245**. Note: b tr of bap, mar and bur 1802, 1804-7 and 1809-12 are held by Lambeth Palace Library, London SE1 7JU.

Indexes 1538-1799, **Ms 11374**, 7 vol.

1. Bap 1538/9-99, mar 1539-99 and bur 1538-99
2. Bap 1600-99
3. Bap 1700-99
4. Mar 1600-99
5. Mar 1700-99
6. Bur 1600-99
7. Bur 1700-99.

Indexes from 1800, **Ms 11366/8-10**, 3 vol.

8. Bap 1800-90, with index to bap of St Magnus the Martyr and St Margaret New Fish Street 1800-91
9. Mar 1800-35, with index to mar of St Magnus the Martyr and St Margaret New Fish Street 1800-91
10. Bur 1800-52, with index to bur of St Magnus the Martyr and St Margaret New Fish Street 1800-53.

ST MICHAEL LE QUERNE

United to St Vedast Foster Lane, 1670

Partial index to bap and mar in **IGI**.

Receipts for bur (with names of deceased) in churchwardens' accounts 1514-1605, **in Ms 2895/1**; 1605-1718, **in Ms 2895/2**; 1718-26, **in Ms 2895/3**.

B tr of bap, mar and bur 1629-30/1, **in Ms 10107**; 1639-39/40, **in Ms 10107A**; 1665-6, **in Ms 10952**. Index: **in Webb 4**.

Bap 1685/6-1812, mar 1686-1705, bur 1685/6-1812: reg damaged beyond repair by enemy action in 1940 and not available for use. Tr and index of bap, mar and bur for these dates, **HS 29-30**. Mar also indexed in **Boyd**. B tr of bap and bur 1803 (Jul.)-1806 (Mar.) and 1807-12, **in Ms 10415/1**.

Bap 1813-84, **Ms 6500**. Indexes: **in HS 29** (to 1836); **in Webb 3** (bap 1837-84 of persons born before 1841).

For later bap, and for mar 1754-1813, see St Vedast Foster Lane.

Mar 1813-36, **Ms 6501**. Indexes: **Boyd**; **in HS 30**.

There are no surviving later mar reg for this parish.

Bur 1813-49, **Ms 6501A**. Indexes: **in HS 30** (to 1837); **in Webb 3** (1838-49); **in Webb 54/1-2** (1813-49).

Transcripts:

Bap, mar and bur 1629-30/1, 1639-39/40 and 1665-6 (from b tr), **Webb 4**. Indexed.

Bap 1685/6-1836, **HS 29**. Indexed.

Mar 1686-1705 and 1813-36, bur 1685/6-1837, **HS 30**. Indexed.

Bur 1838-49, **Webb 3**. Indexed.

B tr of bap, mar and bur 1629-30/1, **in Ms 10107**; bap, mar and bur 1639-39/40, **in Ms 10107A**; bap, mar and bur 1665-6, **in Ms 10952**; bap, mar (from reg of St Vedast Foster Lane with St Michael le Querne) and bur 1803 (Jul.)-1806 (Mar.) and 1807-12, **Ms 10415/1**; bap 1813-57, mar 1813-36, bur 1813-49, **Ms 10415/2**.

ST MICHAEL PATERNOSTER ROYAL

Partial index to bap and mar in **IGI**.

Bap, mar and bur 1558-1653, **Ms 5142**. Indexes: T.C. Dale and J.H. Mann, 'St Michael Paternoster Royal ... register of baptisms ... and burials ...' (typescript, 1934), **GL Printed Books Section**; **Boyd** (mar); T.C. Dale, 'Index to the marriage registers of ... St Michael Paternoster Royal and St Martin Vintry ...' (typescript, also microfilm copy; 1932), **GL Printed Books Section.**

Bap 1653-81/2, mar 1653-66, bur 1653-81/2, **Ms 5143**. Rough bap and bur 1675-81/2, **in Ms 5144** (bap entries apparently identical to those in Ms 5143; some bur entries record fees paid). Indexes: Dale and Mann, as above, **GL Printed Books Section** (bap and bur); **Boyd** (mar); Dale, as above, **GL Printed Books Section** (mar).

Bap and bur 1681/2-1743, **in Ms 5144**. Also contains rough bap and bur 1675-81/2 (for fair reg for these dates see Ms 5143 above), and rough mar 1695-1702 (incomplete; for fair reg to 1701 see St Martin Vintry; for fair reg 1701-43 see Ms 5145 below). Index to Ms 5144: Dale and Mann, as above, **GL Printed Books Section**.

Mar 1675-1701: see St Martin Vintry.

Mar 1701-43 (with St Martin Vintry), **Ms 5145**. Mar to 1710 also **in Ms 5152** (some entries omit details found in Ms 5145). Rough mar 1702, **in Ms 5144** and **in Ms 5153** (both incomplete). Indexes: **Boyd**; Dale, as above, **GL Printed Books Section**.

Bap 1743-1812, mar 1743-54 (with St Martin Vintry), bur 1743-1812, **Ms 5146**. Indexes: Dale and Mann, as above, **GL Printed Books Section** (bap and bur); **Boyd** (mar); Dale, as above, **GL Printed Books Section** (mar).

Bap 1813-1975 (with Allhallows the Great and Allhallows the Less from c.1888, and with St Martin Vintry from c.1906), **Ms 24587**. Index: **in Webb 3** (1813-37; from b tr).

Mar 1754-1812 (with St Martin Vintry), **Ms 5147/1**. Indexes: **Boyd** (except 1776-1800); Dale, as above, **GL Printed Books Section**.

Mar 1813-37, **Ms 5147/2**. Indexes: **Boyd**; Dale, as above, **GL Printed Books Section**.

Mar 1837-1954 (with St Martin Vintry from 1837 and with Allhallows the Great and Allhallows the Less from 1891), **Ms 5147/3**.

Banns 1754-1835 (with St Martin Vintry), **Ms 5149/1**.

Banns 1835-1950 (with St Martin Vintry from 1835 and with Allhallows the Great and Allhallows the Less from 1891), **Ms 5149/2**.

Mar licences collection 1809-1909 (with St Martin Vintry), **Ms 9307/1**. Index: **in Ms 24657** (to 1838).

Mar licences collection 1913-36 (with St Martin Vintry, Allhallows the Great and Allhallows the Less), **Ms 9374**.

Bur 1813-50, **Ms 5148**. Indexes: **in Webb 54/1-2**; Dale and Mann, as above, **GL Printed Books Section**.

Transcripts:

Bap 1558-1812 and bur 1558-1850, Dale and Mann, as above, **GL Printed Books Section**. Indexed.

Mar 1558-1754, **Challen 9**.

Bap 1813-37 and bap 1840-54 of persons born before 1841 (all from b tr), **Webb 3**. Indexed.

B tr of bap 1813-39, mar 1813-36, bur 1813-39, **Ms 11233**; bap 1840-54, bur 1840-50, **Ms 9312**. Note: b tr of bap, mar and bur 1799, 1801-4 and 1811-12 are held by Lambeth Palace Library, London SE1 7JU.

Index to mar 1558-1837, Dale, as above, **GL Printed Books Section**.

ST MICHAEL QUEENHITHE
United to St James Garlickhithe, 1875

Partial index to bap and mar in **IGI**.

Receipts for bur (with names of deceased) 1624-5, 1672-84 and 1690-7, in churchwardens' accounts, **in Ms 4825/1**.

B tr of bap, mar and bur 1639-40, **in Ms 10107A**. Index: **in Webb 16 and 40**.

Bap 1653-1710, mar 1653-1704/5 (with Holy Trinity the Less from 1670), bur 1653-1707, **Ms 9147**. Rough bap from 1694 and mar and bur from 1695, **in Ms 9153/1** (recording fees paid). Index to mar from 1701: **Boyd**.

Bap 1710-37, bur 1707-37, **Ms 9148**. Rough bap and bur to 1711, **in Ms 9153/1** (recording fees paid). Rough bap and bur 1711-34, **in Ms 9153/2** (bur entries record causes of death). Rough bap and bur from 1734, **in Ms 9154** (some bur entries record causes of death and other details not in Ms 9148).

Mar 1705-36 (with Holy Trinity the Less), **Ms 9151/1**. Rough mar to 1711, **in Ms 9153/1** (recording fees paid). Rough mar 1711-34, **in Ms 9153/2**, and from 1734, **in Ms 9154** (entries in both mss apparently identical to those in Ms 9151/1). Index to Ms 9151/1: **Boyd**.

Bap 1737-1812, mar 1737-53 (with Holy Trinity the Less), bur 1737-1812, **Ms 9149**. Rough bap, mar and bur for these dates, **in Ms 9154** (some bur entries record causes of death and other details not in Ms 9149). Index: **Boyd** (mar).

Bap 1813-53 (with Holy Trinity the Less from 1836), **Ms 9150/1**. One bap 1851, **in Ms 9158**. Rough bap to 1830, **in Ms 9154** (recording dates of birth not in Ms 9150/1).

Bap 1854-76 (with Holy Trinity the Less), **Ms 9150/2**.

Mar and banns 1754-95, **Ms 9151/2**. Index: **in Webb 16 and 40**.

Mar and banns 1795-1812 (with Holy Trinity the Less), **in Ms 9159/1**. Index: **in Webb 16 and 40**.

Mar 1813-37 (with Holy Trinity the Less from 1831), **Ms 9151/3**. Index: **in Webb 16 and 40**.

Mar 1837-75 (with Holy Trinity the Less), **Ms 9151/4**.

Banns 1823-75 (with Holy Trinity the Less), **Ms 9160**.

Mar licences collection 1731-2, **Ms 22893**. Index: **Ms 24657**.

Bur 1813-48, **Ms 9152/1**. Rough bur to 1830, **in Ms 9154** (recording causes of death). Index to Ms 9152/1: **in Webb 54/1-2**.

Bur 1848-52, **Ms 9152/2**. Index: **in Webb 54/1-2**.

Later bap and mar in reg of St James Garlickhithe.

Transcripts:

Mar 1653-1753, **Challen 27**.

Mar 1639-40 (from b tr) and 1754-1837, banns 1754-1812, **Webb 16**. Index: **in Webb 16** (places) **and 40** (names).

B tr of bap, mar and bur 1639-40, **in Ms 10107A**; bap, mar and bur 1665-6, **in Ms 10952**; bap, mar and bur 1800, 1801 (Mar.)-1803 (Apr.), 1803 (Jul.)-1805 (May) and 1807-12, **Ms 10443**; bap 1813-60, 1862-75 and 1877-80, mar 1813-36, bur 1813-52 (all with Holy Trinity the Less from 1820), **Ms 11347**.

ST MICHAEL WOOD STREET

United to St Alban Wood Street, 1894; St Vedast Foster Lane, 1954

Partial index to bap and mar in **IGI**.

Bap 1559-1662/3, mar 1559-1661, bur 1559-1659/60, **Ms 6530**. Index: **in Webb 106**.

Bap reg from 1655 destroyed by enemy action in 1940. B tr of bap 1800-11 and 1813-20 (with St Mary Staining from 1813), **in Ms 10416**. Index: **in Webb 106**.

Note: details of destroyed reg taken from Ms 20768 (returns made in 1813 by parishes in the Diocese of London, listing the reg in their care).

Mar 1654-1752 destroyed by enemy action in 1940.

Note: as above.

Mar 1754-1812, banns 1754-1815 (both with St Mary Staining), **Ms 6531**. Indexes: **in Webb 106**; **Boyd** (mar).

Mar 1813-95 (with St Mary Staining): reg destroyed by enemy action in 1940. B tr of mar 1813-20 (with St Mary Staining), **in Ms 10416**. Index: **in Webb 106**. Duplicate reg of mar 1838-95 deposited at the London City Register Office, Finsbury Town Hall, Rosebery Avenue, London EC1R 4QT. Index: **Boyd** (to 1837).

Some mar c.1800-37 in the Pallot Index, held by Achievements Ltd., Northgate, Canterbury, Kent CT1 1BA.

For mar from 1903 see St Alban Wood Street.

Bur 1653-78 destroyed by enemy action in 1940. Receipts for bur (with names of deceased) 1619-78, in churchwardens' accounts, **in Ms 524/1**.

Note: as above.

Bur 1678-1812 (with St Mary Staining), **Ms 6532**. Index: **in Webb 106**.

Note: this register was only recognised to be a joint register with St Mary Staining in 1998. Webb's index therefore assigns the entries to St Michael Wood Street only.

Later bur reg destroyed by enemy action in 1940. B tr of bur 1813-20 (with St Mary Staining), **in Ms 10416**. Indexes: **in Webb 54/1-2** and **in Webb 106**.

Transcripts:

Bap 1559-1662/3, 1800-11 and 1813-20 (with St Mary Staining from 1813), mar 1559-1661 and 1754-1820 (with St Mary Staining from 1754), banns 1754-1815 (with St Mary Staining), bur 1559-1660 (from reg; also from b tr for those years for which no original reg survives), **Webb 12**. Index: **in Webb 106**.

Bur 1559-1660 and 1678-1820 (with St Mary Staining from 1678; 1813-20 from b tr), **Webb 104**. Index: **in Webb 106**. Note: all the entries 1678-1820 are given in Webb under St Michael Wood Street only although they are joint with St Mary Staining.

B tr of bap, mar and bur 1629-29/30, **in Ms 10107**; 1639-39/40, **in Ms 10107A**; 1800-20*, **Ms 10416**.

* St Michael Wood Street with St Mary Staining, except:- 1804, St Michael Wood Street only; 1812, St Mary Staining only.

ST MILDRED BREAD STREET

United to St Mary le Bow, 1954

Partial index to bap and mar in **IGI**.

B tr of bap, mar and bur 1629-30/1, **in Ms 10107**; 1639-39/40, **in Ms 10107A**. Index: **in Webb 4**.

Bap 1658/9-1941: reg destroyed by enemy action in 1941. Tr and index of bap 1658/9-1837, **in HS 42**. Tr of bap 1658/9-1812, **in Ms 12005**. B tr of bap 1800-12, **in Ms 10420/1**; 1813-29 and 1832-42, **in Ms 10420/2**. Index: **in Webb 102** (1838-42).

Mar 1670/1-1754 (with St Margaret Moses): reg destroyed by enemy action in 1941. Tr and index of mar for these dates, **in HS 42**. Tr of mar (not indexed), **in Ms 12005**.

Note: mar for these dates are also indexed in **Boyd**, but this index frequently fails to distinguish between St Mildred Bread Street and St Mildred Poultry, and a number of mar are assigned to the wrong parish.

Mar 1754-1812, banns 1754-74 (both with St Margaret Moses), **Ms 3466**. Indexes: **Boyd**; **in HS 42**.

Mar 1813-37, **Ms 3467**. Indexes: **Boyd**; **in HS 42**.

Mar 1837-1941: reg destroyed by enemy action in 1941. Seven mar 1837-40 entered **in Ms 3467**.

Receipts for bur (with names of deceased) 1648-67, in churchwardens' accounts, **in Ms 3470/1A**.

Bur 1670-1812: reg destroyed by enemy action in 1941. Tr and index of bur for these dates, **in HS 42**. Tr of bur (not indexed), **in Ms 12005**. Receipts for bur (with names of deceased) in churchwardens' accounts: 1741-60, **in Ms 3470/2A/1**; 1760-74, **in Ms 3470/2A/2**; 1774-94, **in Ms 3470/2B/1** (many entries illegible); 1794-1806, **in Ms 3470/2B/2** (many entries illegible). B tr of bur 1800-12, **in Ms 10420/1**.

Bur 1813-53, **Ms 3468**. Indexes: **in HS 42**; **in Webb 54/1-2**.

Transcripts:

Bap, mar and bur 1629-30/1 and 1639-39/40 (from b tr), **Webb 4**. Indexed.

Bap 1658/9-1837, mar 1670/1-1837, banns 1754-74, bur 1670-1853, **HS 42**. Indexed.

Bap 1658/9-1812, mar 1670/1-1812, bur 1670-1812, **Ms 12005**.

Bap 1838-42 (from b tr), **in Webb 102**. Indexed.

B tr of bap, mar and bur 1629-30/1, **in Ms 10107**; bap, mar and bur 1639-39/40, **in Ms 10107A**; bap, mar and bur 1800-12, **Ms 10420/1**; bap 1813-29 and 1832-42, mar 1813-27 and 1832-37, bur 1813-29 and 1832-42, **Ms 10420/2**.

ST MILDRED POULTRY

United to St Olave Jewry, 1871; St Margaret Lothbury, 1886

Partial index to bap and mar in **IGI**.

Bap, mar and bur 1538-1723/4 (mar with St Mary Colechurch from 1670), **Ms 4429/1**. Includes mar 1683/4-84 at Mercers' Hall Chapel. Index: **Boyd** (mar).

Note: Boyd's index frequently fails to distinguish between St Mildred Poultry and St Mildred Bread Street, and a number of mar are assigned to the wrong parish.

Bap 1724-1812, mar 1724-54 (with St Mary Colechurch), bur 1724-1812, **Ms 4429/2**. Index: **Boyd** (mar).

See note above.

Bap 1813-70 (with St Mary Colechurch), **Ms 4430**.

Mar 1754-1812, banns 1756-65 (both with St Mary Colechurch), **Ms 4434**. Index: **in Webb 17 and 40**.

Mar 1813-37 (with St Mary Colechurch), **Ms 4431/1**. Index: **in Webb 17 and 40**.

Mar 1837-71 (with St Mary Colechurch), **Ms 4431/2**.

Banns 1792-1811 (with St Mary Colechurch), **Ms 4347A**.

Banns 1812-65 (with St Mary Colechurch), **Ms 4435**. Fair copy of banns 1833-47, **in Ms 4433**.

Banns 1870 (with St Mary Colechurch), **in Ms 4433**.

Mar licences collection 1810-70 (with St Mary Colechurch), **Ms 24137**. Index: **in Ms 24657** (to 1838).

Bur 1813-52 (with St Mary Colechurch), **Ms 4432**. Index: **in Webb 54/1-2**.

For later bap, mar and banns see St Olave Jewry.

Transcripts:

Mar 1538-1754, **Challen 8**.

Mar 1754-1837, banns 1756-65, **Webb 17**. Index: **in Webb 17** (places) **and 40** (names).

B tr of bap, mar and bur 1800, 1802-3, 1807-11 and 1813-33 (mar from 1800 and bap and bur from 1811 with St Mary Colechurch), **Ms 10438**.

ST NICHOLAS ACONS
United to St Edmund the King and Martyr, 1670

Partial index to bap and mar in **IGI**.

Bap 1539/40-1812, mar 1539-1664, bur 1540-1812, **Ms 17621**. Bur accounts 1759-90, **Ms 18491**. Rough bap and bur from 1804, **in Ms 11440** (with some variant entries and omissions). Indexes to Ms 17621: **Boyd** (mar); in W. Brigg, *The register book of the parish of St Nicholas Acons* (Leeds, 1890), **GL Printed Books Section**.

Bap 1813-75, **Ms 17622**. Rough bap to 1820, **in Ms 11440**, and 1820-64, **in Ms 11441** (both with some variant entries and omissions). Index to bap 1813-41: **in Webb 1**.

Mar 1673-1812: see St Edmund the King and Martyr.

Mar 1813-37, **Ms 17623**. Index: **in Webb 1**.

Mar 1837-49, **Ms 20209**.

Bur 1813-48, **Ms 17624**. Rough bur to 1820, **in Ms 11440**, and 1820-48, **in Ms 11442** (both with some variant entries and omissions). Index: **in Webb 1 and 54/1-2** (note: Webb 1 compiled from b tr and rough reg, not from original reg).

Later bap and mar, also banns from 1811, entered in reg of St Edmund the King and Martyr.

Transcripts:

Bap 1539/40-1812, mar 1539-1664, bur 1540-1812, W. Brigg, *The register book of the parish of St Nicholas Acons* (Leeds, 1890), **GL Printed Books Section**. Indexed.

Bap 1813-41, mar 1813-37, bur 1813-48, **Webb 1**. Indexed. Note: compiled from b tr of bap, mar and bur (Mss 10454-4A) and from rough reg of bap and bur (Mss 11440-2), not from original reg.

B tr of bap, mar and bur 1629-30/1, **in Ms 10107**; bap, mar and bur 1639-39/40, **in Ms 10107A**; bap 1800, mar 1800-3 and 1808, bur 1800 and 1808, **in Ms 10453**; bap 1801-3 and 1807-37, mar 1809-37, bur 1801-3, 1807 and 1809-37, **Ms 10454**; bap 1838-42, 1844-8 and 1851-60, bur 1838-42 and 1844-8, **Ms 10454A**; bap 1843 and 1849-50, bur 1843, **in Ms 10453A**.

ST NICHOLAS COLE ABBEY

Partial index to bap and mar in **IGI**.

Bap 1538/9-1650, mar 1584-1650/1, bur 1538-1647, **Ms 5685**. Index: **Boyd** (mar).

Bap, mar and bur 1650/1-95 (with St Nicholas Olave from c.1670), **in Ms 5686**. Index: **Boyd** (mar).

Bap 1695-1747, mar 1695-1718, bur 1695-1747/8 (all with St Nicholas Olave to 1704), **Ms 5687**. Births of 'children ... not christened according to the Church of England' 1698-1701, **in Ms 5686**. Index: **Boyd** (mar).

Bap 1748-1812, **Ms 5688**.

Bap 1813-1975, **Ms 9359**.

Note: this is a joint reg with St Mary Somerset, St Mary Mounthaw, St Benet Paul's Wharf and St Peter Paul's Wharf from c.1887 and with St Nicholas Olave from c.1936; there is also a separate reg of bap from 1879 of the Welsh congregation at St Benet Paul's Wharf, *q.v.*

Mar 1718-53 (with St Nicholas Olave from 1721), **Ms 5689**. Index: **Boyd**.

Mar 1755-1812 (with St Nicholas Olave), **Ms 5690/1**. Index: **Boyd**.

Mar 1813-37, **Ms 5690/2**. Index: **in Webb 17 and 40**.

Mar 1837-1946 (with St Nicholas Olave, also, from 1879, with St Mary Somerset, St Mary Mounthaw, St Benet Paul's Wharf and St Peter Paul's Wharf), **Ms 5690/3**. One mar 1873, **in Ms 5690/2**.

Banns 1754-1889 (with St Nicholas Olave, also, from 1877, with St Mary Somerset and St Mary Mounthaw, and, from 1879, with St Benet Paul's Wharf and St Peter Paul's Wharf), **Ms 5691**.

Bur 1748-1812, **Ms 5692/1**.

Bur 1813-51, **Ms 5692/2**. Index: **in Webb 54/1-2**.

Transcripts:

Mar 1813-37 and 1873, **Webb 17**. Index: **in Webb 17** (places) **and 40** (names).

B tr of bap, mar and bur 1639-39/40, **in Ms 10107A**; bap, mar and bur 1665-6, **in Ms 10952**; bap, mar and bur 1800-2, 1803 (Mar.)-1804 (Mar.), 1807-8 and 1809 (Aug.)-1811, **in Ms 10432**; bap, mar and bur 1812-20 (with St Nicholas Olave), **Ms 10432A**; bap 1821-31 and 1833-42, mar 1821-31 and 1833-7, bur 1821-31 and 1833-42, **Ms 10432B**; bap and bur 1843-5 (with St Nicholas Olave), **Ms 10432C**.

ST NICHOLAS OLAVE

United to St Nicholas Cole Abbey, 1670

Partial index to bap and mar in **IGI**.

Bap, mar and bur c.1670-1704: see St Nicholas Cole Abbey.

Bap 1704-1812, mar 1705-20, bur 1704-1812, **Ms 5696**. Rough bap 1704-14, mar 1705-13 and bur 1704-14, **Ms 5697** (with some variant entries). Index to both mss: **in Webb 2**.

Bap 1813-1908 and 1936 (one entry only for St Nicholas Cole Abbey), **Ms 5698**. Index: **in Webb 2** (to 1840).

Mar 1721-1812: see St Nicholas Cole Abbey.

Mar 1813-36, **Ms 5699**. Index: **in Webb 2**.

Bur 1813-52, **Ms 5700**. Index: **in Webb 2 and 54/1-2**.

For later bap and mar, and for banns 1754-1889, see St Nicholas Cole Abbey.

Transcripts:

Bap 1704-1840, bap 1841-1936 of persons born before 1841, mar 1705-20 and 1813-36, bur 1704-1852, **Webb 2**. Indexed.

B tr of bap, mar and bur 1800-3, 1807-8 and 1810-11, **Ms 10414**; mar 1809-10, **in Ms 10432**; bap, mar and bur 1812-20, **in Ms 10432A**; bap 1821-42, mar 1821-31 and 1833-6, bur 1821-42, **Ms 10414A**; bap and bur 1843-5, **in Ms 10432C**.

ST NICHOLAS SHAMBLES

Amalgamated with St Ewin to form Christchurch Newgate Street, 1547

Bap, mar and bur 1538-47, **in Ms 9264**. From 1547 this vol contains registrations for Christchurch Newgate Street, *q.v.* Tr and index: **HS 21**.

ST OLAVE HART STREET

Partial index to bap and mar in **IGI**.

Bap 1563-1631, mar 1563-1633, bur 1563-1633, **Ms 28867**. Indexes: **in HS 46**; **Boyd** (mar).

Bap 1631-1706/7, **Ms 28868**. Index: **in HS 46** (to 1700/1).

Mar 1633-1704, bur 1633-84, **Ms 28869**. Indexes: **in HS 46** (to 1700/1); **Boyd** (mar).

Bap 1706/7-1812, mar 1704-54, **Ms 17818**. Duplicate bap 1801-12, **Ms 17819**. Index to mar: **Boyd**.

Bap 1813-1978 (with Allhallows Staining from 1870 and with St Katherine Coleman from 1922), **Ms 21550**.

Mar and banns 1754-76, **Ms 17820/1**.

Mar 1776-1808, banns 1776-1815, **Ms 17820/2**.

Mar 1809-1961 (with Allhallows Staining from 1870 and with St Katherine Coleman from 1922), **Ms 17821**, 4 vol.

1. 1809-37* 2. 1837-1929 3. 1929-37 4. 1937-61.

*includes mar 1837-56, as in Ms 17821/2 (with less detail; giving parishes rather than precise addresses of parties).

Banns 1823-6 and 1840-1936 (with Allhallows Staining from 1870 and with St Katherine Coleman from 1922), **Ms 17822**.

Bur 1684-1805, **Ms 28870**. Index: **in HS 46** (to 1700/1).

Bur 1805-12, **Ms 17823/1**. Includes tr of bur 1801-5, from Ms 28870.

Bur 1813-53, **Ms 17823/2**. Includes interments of ashes 1959-64. Index to bur: in J. Hanson and M. Stevens, *City of London burial index 1813-1853 part 3* (Milton Keynes, 1997?), fiches 104, **GL Printed Books Section**.

Transcripts:

Bap, mar and bur 1563-1700/1, **HS 46**. Indexed.

Mar 1701-54, **Challen 12**.

B tr of bap, mar and bur 1629-29/30, **in Ms 10107**; bap, mar and bur 1665-65/6, **in Ms 10952**; bap 1802-11, mar and bur 1802-12, **Ms 10413/1**; bap 1813-37, mar 1813-35, bur 1813-37, **Ms 10413/2**; bap and bur 1838-46, **Ms 10413/3**.

ST OLAVE JEWRY

United to St Margaret Lothbury, 1886

Partial index to bap and mar in **IGI**.

Bap 1538/9-1629/30, mar 1538/9-1632/3, bur 1538-1629/30, **Ms 4399**. Parchment copy from 1558, **in Ms 4400/1**. Index: **Boyd** (mar).

Bap 1630-60, mar 1632/3-53/4, bur 1630-72, **in Ms 4400/1**. Includes tr of bap, mar and bur from 1558, from Ms 4399. One mar 1637/8, **in Ms 4399**. Index: **Boyd** (mar).

Bap 1660-85/6, mar 1653/4-1754 (with St Martin Pomeroy from c.1670), bur 1672-85/6, **Ms 4400/2**. Index: **Boyd** (mar).

Bap and bur 1686-1812, **Ms 4401/1**.

Bap 1813-18, **Ms 4406**. Tr in Ms 4401/2.

Bap 1819-84 (with St Mildred Poultry and St Mary Colechurch from c.1871), **in Ms 4401/2**. Includes tr of bap 1813-18, from Ms 4406.

For later bap see St Margaret Lothbury.

Mar 1754-1812, banns 1771-1803 (both with St Martin Pomeroy), **Ms 4402**. Index: **in Webb 16 and 40**.

Mar 1813-18 (with St Martin Pomeroy), **Ms 4403**. Tr in Ms 4404. Index: **in Webb 16 and 40**.

Mar 1818-37 (with St Martin Pomeroy), **Ms 4404**. Includes tr of mar 1813-18, from Ms 4403. Index: **in Webb 16 and 40**.

Mar 1838-86 (with St Martin Pomeroy; also, from c.1871, with St Mildred Poultry and St Mary Colechurch), **Ms 4407**.

Banns 1824-50 (with St Martin Pomeroy), **Ms 4405/1**.

Banns 1852-86 (with St Martin Pomeroy; also, from c.1871, with St Mildred Poultry and St Mary Colechurch), **Ms 4405/2**.

For later mar, banns and mar licences from 1886, see St Margaret Lothbury.

Bur 1813-17, **Ms 4408**. Tr in Ms 4401/2.

Bur 1819-49, **in Ms 4401/2**. Includes tr of bur 1813-17, from Ms 4408. Index: **in Webb 54/1-2**.

Transcripts:

Mar 1538/9-1754, **Challen 8**.

Mar 1754-1837, banns 1771-1803, **Webb 16**. Index: **in Webb 16** (places) **and 40** (names).

B tr of bap, mar and bur 1629-30/1, **in Ms 10107**; bap, mar and bur 1800-1, 1802 (Mar.)-1803 (Mar.) and 1807-12 (mar 1812 with St Martin Pomeroy), **Ms 11509**; bap 1813-18, 1832-7, 1854-6 and 1858, mar and bur 1813-18 and 1832-7 (all with St Martin Pomeroy), **Ms 14567**.

ST OLAVE SILVER STREET

United to St Alban Wood Street, 1670; St Vedast Foster Lane, 1954

Partial index to bap in **IGI**.

Bap 1562-1770, mar 1562-1680, bur 1561-1770, **Ms 6534**. Photographs, taken under ultra-violet light, of illegible pages (only) in this reg, **Ms 6534A**. Tr of both mss **in Webb 105**. Index: **in Webb 106**.

Bap 1770-1812: reg damaged beyond repair by enemy action in 1940, and not available for use. Tr of bap 1770 (Oct.)-1772 (Nov.) and 1773 (Oct.)-1774 (Sep.), **Ms 18630** (indexed). B tr of bap 1800-5 and 1807-12, **in Ms 11238**. Index to both tr: **in Webb 106**.

Mar 1681-1811: for main series of registrations, see St Alban Wood Street. Two mar 1743, **in Ms 6534**. Index: **in Webb 106**.

B tr of mar 1811-12, **in Ms 11238**.

Bur 1770-1812: reg damaged beyond repair by enemy action in 1940, and not available for use. One bur 1773, **in Ms 6534**. Receipts for bur (with names of deceased) 1757-93, in churchwardens' accounts, **in Ms 1257/4**. B tr of bur 1800-5 and 1807-12, **in Ms 11238**. Index to Mss 6354 and 11238: **in Webb 106**.

For later reg see St Alban Wood Street.

Transcripts:

Bap 1562-1774, 1800-5 and 1807-12, mar 1562-1680 and 1743, bur 1561-1770, 1773, 1800-5 and 1807-12 (from reg; also from b tr for those years for which no original reg survive), **in Webb 105**. Index: **in Webb 106**.

B tr of bap, mar and bur 1639-39/40, **in Ms 10107A**; 1665-65/6, **in Ms 10952**; 1800-5 and 1807-12 (mar from reg of St Alban Wood Street with St Olave Silver Street), **Ms 11238**. Index: **in Webb 106** (bap and bur 1800-12).

ST PANCRAS SOPER LANE

United to St Mary le Bow, 1670

Partial index to bap and mar in **IGI**.

Bap 1538-1697/8, mar 1538-1674, bur 1538-1697, **Ms 5015**. Indexes: **Boyd** (mar); **in HS 44-5** (bap, mar and bur).

Bap 1697/8-1812, mar 1675-1812, banns 1754-1937, bur 1697/8-1812: see St Mary le Bow.

Bap 1813-89, **Ms 5015A**. Indexes: **in HS 44-5** (to 1837); **in Webb 3** (bap 1838-89 of persons born before 1841).

For later bap see St Mary le Bow.

Mar 1818-36, **Ms 5016**. Indexes: **Boyd**; **in HS 45**.

Bur 1813-49, **Ms 5017**. Indexes: **in HS 44-5**; **in Webb 54/1-2**.

Later mar entered in reg of St Mary le Bow.

Transcripts:

Bap 1538-1697/8 and 1813-37, bur 1538-1697 and 1813-49, **HS 44**. Indexed **in HS 45**.

Mar 1538-1674 and 1818-36, **HS 45**. Indexed.

Bap 1667-97, mar 1672/3-74, bur 1668-97, **in Ms 4997**.

B tr of bap 1817-46 and 1848-58, mar 1818-36, bur 1818-46 and 1848-9, **in Ms 14565**.

ST PAUL'S CATHEDRAL (non-parochial)

Mar 1697-1740, **Ms 25740**. Indexes: **Boyd**; **in HS 26**; **in Ms 25743/2**.

Receipts for bur (with names of deceased) in chamberlains' accounts 1525-6, **in Ms 25634**; 1535-6, **in Ms 25635**; 1548-50, **in Ms 25636**; 1554-5, **in Ms 25637/1**; 1555-7, **in Ms 25637/2**; 1570-84, **in Ms 25498**; 1592-4, **in Ms 25638**.

Some registrations of bur at St Paul's Cathedral in the reg of St Gregory by St Paul 1559-1626/7, **Ms 10231**.

Bur 1706, 1734/5 and 1760-1812 (with three deleted entries 1814), **Ms 25741**. Rough bur 1760-1812, **in Ms 25742** (entries apparently identical to those in Ms 25741). Indexes: **in HS 26**; **in Ms 25743/3**.

Other reg (bap 1708-13 and 1875-1975, mar 1740-1982 [none recorded 7 Feb. 1758 to 9 Aug. 1877], bur 1814-date) held in St Paul's Cathedral Library, London EC4M 8AE to which written application should be made. The following are available at GL:

Tr and index of bap 1708-13 and 1875-97, mar 1697-1758 and 1877-96, bur 1760-1899, **HS 26**.
Index of bap 1708-13 and 1875-1939, **Ms 25743/1**.
Index of mar 1697-1758 and 1877-1939, **Ms 25743/2**.

Index of mar 1697-1758, **Boyd**.
Mar licences collection 1877-1980, **Ms 21648/1-21** (detailed list available).
Tr and index of bur 1813-53: M. Stevens (reproduction of typescript held by the Society of Genealogists; 1996), fo pam 8935, **GL Printed Books Section**. Also indexed in J. Hanson and M. Stevens, *City of London burial index 1813-1853 part 3* (Milton Keynes, 1997?), fiches 104, **GL Printed Books Section**.
B tr of bur 1814-20 and 1825-38, **Ms 11232**.
Index of bur 1760-1936, **Ms 25743/3**.

ST PETER CORNHILL

Partial index to bap and mar in **IGI**.

Bap 1538-1774, mar 1538/9-1754, bur 1538/9-1774, **Ms 8820**. Indexes: **Boyd** (mar); **in HS 1 and 4** (bap, mar and bur).

Bap and bur 1775-1812, **Ms 8821**. Bur accounts from 1781, **in Ms 4171**. Index to Ms 8821: **in Webb 10**.

Bap 1813-1951, **Ms 8822**. Index: **in Webb 10** (to 1840).

Mar 1754-80, **Ms 8823/1**. Index: **in Webb 10**.

Mar 1781-1812, **Ms 8823/2**. Index: **in Webb 10**.

Mar 1813-37, **Ms 8823/3**. Index: **in Webb 10**.

Mar 1837-1985, **Ms 8823/4**.

Banns 1754-1821, **Ms 8825/1**.

Banns 1821-5, **Ms 8825/2**.

Banns 1826-1977, **Ms 8825/3**.

Bur 1813-53, **Ms 8824**. Bur accounts to 1848, **in Ms 4171**. Index to Ms 8824: **in Webb 10 and 54/1-2**.

Transcripts:

Bap 1538-1774, mar 1538/9-1754, bur 1538/9-1774, **HS 1 and 4**. Indexed.

Bap 1775-1840, bap 1841-1951 of persons born before 1841, mar 1754-1837, bur 1775-1853, **Webb 10**. Indexed.

B tr of bap, mar and bur 1639-39/40, **in Ms 10107A**; bap, mar and bur 1800, 1801 (Apr.)-1804 (Apr.) and 1808-12, **Ms 10433**; bap 1813-60 and 1862-93, mar 1813-60 and 1862-91, bur 1813-53, **Ms 11348**.

ST PETER LE POER
United to St Michael Cornhill, 1906

Partial index to bap and mar in **IGI**.

Bap, mar and bur 1561-1723, banns 1653-5, **Ms 4093/1**. Indexes: **Boyd** (mar); in J.F. Bromley, 'St Peter le Poer: Transcript of ... the original registers' (typescript, 1971), **GL Printed Books Section** (bap, mar and bur).

Bap 1723-1812, mar 1723-54, bur 1723-1812, **Ms 4093/2**. Indexes: **Boyd** (mar); in Bromley, as above, **GL Printed Books Section** (bap, mar and bur).

Bap 1813-29, **Ms 4095/1**. Index: in Bromley, as above, **GL Printed Books Section**.

Bap 1830-1905 (with St Benet Fink from 1846), **Ms 4095/2**. One bap 1863 and one bap 1880, **in Ms 4102/2**. Index: in Bromley, as above, **GL Printed Books Section** (to 1840).

For later bap see St Michael Cornhill.

Mar and banns 1755-71, **Ms 4094/1**. Indexes: Boyd (mar and banns); in Bromley, as above, **GL Printed Books Section** (mar).

Mar 1771-1812, banns 1771-1817, **Ms 4094/2**. Indexes: **Boyd** (mar and banns, except 1776-1800); in Bromley, as above, **GL Printed Books Section** (mar).

Mar 1813-28, **Ms 4094/3**. Indexes: **Boyd**; in Bromley, as above, **GL Printed Books Section**.

Mar 1830-7, **Ms 4094/4**. Indexes: **Boyd**; in Bromley, as above, **GL Printed Books Section**.

Mar 1837-1904 (with St Benet Fink from 1846), **Ms 4094/5**. Index: in Bromley, as above, **GL Printed Books Section** (to 1840).

Bur 1813-29, **Ms 4096/1**. Indexes: in Bromley, as above, **GL Printed Books Section**; in J. Hanson and M. Stevens, *City of London burial index 1813-1853 part 3* (Milton Keynes, 1997?), fiches 104, **GL Printed Books Section**.

Bur 1830-53 (with St Benet Fink from 1846), **Ms 4096/2**. Indexes: in Bromley, as above, **GL Printed Books Section** (to 1840); in Hanson and Stevens, as above, **GL Printed Books Section**.

Later mar entered in reg of St Michael Cornhill.

Transcripts:

Bap, mar and bur 1561-1840, Bromley, as above, **GL Printed Books Section**. Indexed.

Mar 1561-1837, banns 1755-1817, **Challen 7**.

B tr of bap 1809-30, 1832-3, 1838-41 and 1845-90, mar 1809-30 and 1832-3, bur 1809-30, 1832-3, 1838-41 and 1845-53 (all with St Benet Fink from 1846), **Ms 14568**.

ST PETER PAUL'S WHARF

United to St Benet Paul's Wharf, 1670; St Nicholas Cole Abbey, 1879

Partial index to bap and mar in **IGI**.

Bap 1607-53, mar 1607-22 and 1625-49, bur 1607-53, **Ms 5721/1**. Indexes: **Boyd** (mar); **in HS 38** (bap); **in HS 40** (mar); **in HS 41** (bur).

Mar 1622-5, **Ms 5721A**. Indexes: **Boyd**; **in HS 40**.

Bap 1653-1809, mar 1653-60, bur 1653-77, **Ms 5721/2**. Additional bap 1695-1706, in a vol whose present location is unknown, transcribed **in HS 38**. Indexes: **Boyd** (mar); **in HS 38** (bap); **in HS 40** (mar); **in HS 41** (bur).

Bap 1809-12, **Ms 5722/1**. Index: **in HS 38**.

Bap 1813-86, **Ms 5722/2**. Indexes: **in HS 38** (to 1837); **in Webb 3** (bap 1838-86 of persons born before 1841).

Mar c.1680-1879: for main series of registrations see St Benet Paul's Wharf. One mar 1684, **in Ms 5721/2**; eleven mar 1698-1704/5, in a vol whose present location is unknown, transcribed **in HS 40**; three mar 1828-34, **Ms 5723**. These fifteen mar are indexed in **Boyd** and **in HS 40**.

Bur 1678-1810, **Ms 5724**. Index: **in HS 41**.

Note: four additional bur 1683/4-85 are entered (inverted) at back of Ms 5724. Also at back are duplicate bur 1689-1708/9, recording affidavits of bur in woollen. Vol (present location unknown) containing duplicate bur 1709-33, and recording affidavits of bur in woollen, transcribed **in HS 41**.

Bur 1810-12, **Ms 5725/1**. Index: **in HS 41**.

Bur 1813-48, **Ms 5725/2**. Indexes: **in HS 41** (to 1837); **in Webb 3** (1838-49); **in Webb 54/1-2** (1813-49).

For later bap and mar see St Nicholas Cole Abbey.

Transcripts:

Bap 1607-1837, **HS 38**. Indexed.

Mar 1607-60, 1684, 1698-1704/5 and 1828-34, **HS 40**. Indexed.

Bur 1607-1837, **HS 41**. Indexed.

Bur 1838-49, **Webb 3**. Indexed.

B tr of bap 1800-51 and 1854-65, mar 1802, 1805-8 and 1810-11 (from reg of St Benet Paul's Wharf with St Peter Paul's Wharf), bur 1800-49, **Ms 10419**; bap 1867-72, **Ms 5722A**.

ST PETER WESTCHEAP

United to St Matthew Friday Street, 1670; St Vedast Foster Lane, 1882

Partial index to bap and mar in **IGI**.

Bap, mar and bur 1538-98, **Ms 6502** (now incomplete and partly illegible following damage by enemy action in 1940). Tr of mar for these dates (made before reg was damaged), **in Challen 12**; indexed in **Boyd**. Tr of bap and bur for these dates (made from damaged reg), **in Webb 102**; indexed. No complete tr of bap and bur is known; for sources which may be of use in tracing bap and bur where Ms 6502 is deficient, see next paragraph.

Bap and bur c.1599-1812: reg destroyed by enemy action in 1940. The following sources are available:

> Receipts for bur (with names of deceased) in churchwardens' accounts, 1534-1601, **in Ms 645/1**; 1601-71 and 1681-99, **in Ms 645/2**; 1702-21, 1730-2, 1739-54 and 1762-3, **in Ms 645/3**.
>
> Tr of extracts from bap and bur 1538-1812, held by the Archivist, College of Arms, Queen Victoria Street, London EC4V 4BT (in Chester Ms 48; available by appointment only).
>
> Tr of extracts from bap 1554-1797, bur 1542-1791, **in Ms 3713/1**. Index: **in Webb 102** (1599-1626 and 1632-1797).

B tr of bap, mar and bur 1629-30/1, **in Ms 10107**. Index: **in Webb 102** (bap and bur).

B tr of bap and bur 1800-2 (Apr.) and 1807-11, **in Ms 14569**. Index: **in Webb 102**.

Bap 1813-76, **Ms 6503**. Index: **in Webb 2** (1813-40).

For bap from 1882 see St Vedast Foster Lane.

Mar 1598/9-1698/9: reg destroyed by enemy action in 1940. Tr of mar 1538-1698/9, **in Challen 12**; indexed in **Boyd**.

Mar c.1699-1812: entered in reg of St Matthew Friday Street, which were destroyed by enemy action in 1940. Tr **in HS 63** (indexed) and **in Challen 12**; also indexed in **Boyd** (except 1776-1800). B tr of mar 1800-2 (Apr.) and 1807-11, **in Ms 14569**.

Mar 1814-36, **Ms 6504**. Index: **Boyd**.

For mar from 1837 see St Matthew Friday Street.

Bur 1813-46, **Ms 6505** (now incomplete following damage by enemy action in 1940). B tr of bur 1813-44, **in Ms 10451**. The reg and b tr are transcribed, collated and indexed **in Webb 2**. Index to Ms 6505: **in Webb 54/1-2**.

Transcripts:

Bap and bur 1538-98 (made from damaged reg), **in Webb 102**. Indexed.

Mar 1538-1698/9 and 1814-36, **Challen 12**.

Bap and bur 1629-30/1, 1800-2 and 1807-11 (from b tr), **in Webb 102**. Indexed.

Bap 1813-40, bap 1841-7 of persons born before 1841, bur 1813-46, **Webb 2**. Indexed.

Bap 1857-76, **in Ms 10955**.

B tr of bap, mar and bur 1629-30/1, **in Ms 10107**; bap, mar and bur 1800-2 (Apr.) and 1807-11 (mar from reg of St Matthew Friday Street with St Peter Westcheap), **Ms 14569**; bap 1813-44 and 1848-55, mar 1814-36, bur 1813-44, **in Ms 10451**.

ST SEPULCHRE HOLBORN (also known as HOLY SEPULCHRE WITHOUT NEWGATE)

Partial index to bap in **IGI**.

Bap and mar 1662-78, bur 1662-77, **Ms 7219/1**. Indexes: **Boyd** (mar); **in Ms 7225** (mar).

Bap 1678/9-92/3, mar 1678/9-1701, bur 1677-91/2, **Ms 7219/2**. Indexes: **Boyd** (mar); **in Ms 7225** (mar).

Bap 1692/3-1714, mar 1701-14, bur 1691/2-1714, **Ms 7219/3**. Indexes: **Boyd** (mar); **in Ms 7225** (mar).

Bap, mar and bur 1714-31, **Ms 7219/4**. Indexes: **Boyd** (mar); **in Ms 7225** (mar).

Bap and mar 1731-51/2, **Ms 7220/1**. Indexes: **Boyd** (mar); **in Ms 7225** (mar).

Bap 1751/2-68, mar 1752-4, **Ms 7220/2**. Indexes: **Boyd** (mar); **in Ms 7225** (mar).

Bap 1768-1987, **Ms 7221**, 8 vol.

1. 1768-87	3. 1808-12	5. 1818-31	7. 1852-86
2. 1787-1808*	4. 1813-18	6. 1832-52	8. 1886-1987.

*Photocopy on Reading Room shelves, **Ms 7221/2A**.

Indexes: **Ms 7224/1** (1832-51); **Ms 7224/2** (1852-86).

Mar 1754-1981, **Ms 7222**, 18 vol.

1. 1754-64	6. 1813-24	11. 1855-62	16. 1933-49
2. 1764-76	7. 1824-37	12. 1862-71	17. 1950-71
3. 1776-86	8. 1837-42	13. 1871-82	18. 1971-81.
4. 1786-1802	9. 1842-8	14. 1883-1901	
5. 1802-12	10. 1848-55	15. 1901-33	

Banns 1883-1902 and 1946-82, **Ms 31569**, 3 vol.

1. 1883-91	2. 1891-1902	3. missing	4. 1946-82.

Bur 1731-1857, **Ms 7223**, 7 vol.

1. 1731-52	3. 1774-92	5. 1813-21	7. 1842-57.
2. 1752-74	4. 1792-1812	6. 1821-42	

Index: **Webb 36** (1813-57).

Rough bur 1818-31, **Ms 9443**; 1836-40, **Ms 3164/1**; 1840-51, **Ms 3164/3** (all recording places of interment and undertakers' names). Rough bur 1838-57, **Ms 3164/2** (similar to the preceding, but also recording undertakers' addresses, depths of graves etc; indexed 1838-49).

Funerals 1900-4, **in Mss 7223-7** (recording cemeteries where interred). Index: **in Webb 36**.

Transcripts:

Mar 1662-1754, **Challen 14**. Another copy, with ms index, **Ms 7225**.

B tr of bap 1800-47, 1855, 1857-60 and 1862-91, mar 1800-47, 1855 and 1857-60, bur 1800-47, 1855 and 1857, **Ms 11337**, 10 boxes (list available at Mss enquiry desk).

B tr (parish copies, completed but not returned to the diocese) of bap, mar and bur 1848-54 and 1856, **Ms 7226**, 8 vol (list available at Mss enquiry desk).

ST STEPHEN COLEMAN STREET
United to St Margaret Lothbury, 1954

Partial index to bap and mar in **IGI**.

Receipts for bur (with names of deceased) 1486-1507, in churchwardens' accounts, **in Ms 4457/1**.

Bap, mar and bur 1538-98, **Ms 4448**. Parchment copy 1558-98, **in Ms 4449/1**.

Bap, mar and bur 1598-1636, **in Ms 4449/1**.

Bap and mar 1636-1717, bur 1636-89, **Ms 4449/2**. Index: **Boyd** (mar from 1701).

Bap 1717-1802, mar 1717-54, **Ms 4450**. Index: **Boyd** (mar).

Bap 1803-1951, **Ms 4454**, 4 vol.
1. 1803-12 2. 1813-39 3. 1840-73 4. 1873-1951.

Mar 1754-1952, **Ms 4452**, 4 vol.
1. 1754-1812 2. 1813-37 3. 1837-65 4. 1865-1952.

Banns 1754-1847, **Ms 4453**.

Mar licences collection 1813-1910, **Ms 9456**, 3 boxes.
1. 1813-35 2. 1836-59 3. 1860-1910.
Index: **in Ms 24657** (to 1838).

Bur 1689-1812, **Ms 4451/1**. Deaths 1711-23**, Ms 4455** (recording dates, places and causes of death, but omitting dates and places of bur).

Bur 1813-53, **Ms 4451/2**. Bur accounts 1835-53, **Ms 8844**. Index to Ms 4451/2: in J. Hanson and M. Stevens, *City of London burial index 1813-1853 part 3* (Milton Keynes, 1997?), fiches 104, **GL Printed Books Section**.

Transcripts:

Mar 1538-1754, **Challen 25**.

B tr of bap, mar and bur 1800-2 and 1807-11, **Ms 10444**; bap 1813-46, 1849-60 and 1862-9, mar 1813-37, bur 1813-46 and 1849, **Ms 10444A**.

ST STEPHEN WALBROOK

Partial index to bap and mar in **IGI**.

Receipts for bur (with names of deceased) in churchwardens' accounts c.1474-1538, **in Ms 593/1**; 1548-1636/7, **in Ms 593/2**.

Bap, mar and bur 1557-1716 (with St Benet Sherehog from c.1670), **Ms 8319/1**. Indexes: **Boyd** (mar); **in HS 49-50** (bap, mar and bur).

Bap 1716-90, mar 1716-54, bur 1716-90 (all with St Benet Sherehog), **Ms 8319/2**. Includes one bap 1797, duplicate of an entry in Ms 8320. Indexes: **Boyd** (mar); **in HS 49-50** (bap, mar and bur).

Bap and bur 1790-1812 (with St Benet Sherehog), **Ms 8320**. Index: **in HS 50**.

Bap 1813-1946 (with St Benet Sherehog), **Ms 8321**. Indexes: **in HS 50** (to 1860); **in Webb 3** (bap from 1861 of persons born before 1841).

Mar 1754-1804 (with St Benet Sherehog), **Ms 8322/1**. Indexes: **Boyd**; **in HS 50**.

Mar 1804-12 (with St Benet Sherehog), **Ms 8322/2**. Indexes: in reg; **Boyd**; **in HS 50**.

Mar 1813-37 (with St Benet Sherehog), **Ms 8322/3**. Includes mar 1837-42, as in Ms 8322/4 (with less detail; giving parishes rather than precise addresses of parties). Indexes: **Boyd** (to 1837); **in HS 50**.

Mar 1837-1940 (with St Benet Sherehog), **Ms 8322/4**. Index: **in HS 50** (to 1860).

Banns 1754-1841 (with St Benet Sherehog), **Ms 8324/1**. Indexes: **Boyd** (to 1837); **in HS 50**.

Banns 1841-52 (with St Benet Sherehog), **Ms 8324/2**.

Banns 1852-1954 (with St Benet Sherehog), **Ms 8324/3**.

Bur 1813-60 (with St Benet Sherehog), **Ms 8323**. Indexes: **in HS 50**; **in Webb 54/1-2**.

Later bap and mar reg retained by incumbent.

Transcripts:

Bap, mar and bur 1557-1860, banns 1754-1841, **HS 49-50**. Indexed.

B tr of bap, mar and bur 1665-65/6, **in Ms 10952**; 1800-3 and 1806-37, **Ms 11240**.

ST SWITHIN LONDON STONE

United to St Stephen Walbrook, 1954

Partial index to bap in **IGI**.

Bap 1615-75, mar 1619-65, bur 1614-65, **Ms 4311**. Tr (contemporary) of bur 1656-65, **in Ms 4312**.

Note: entries in Ms 4311 are in disorder - see note at front of vol concerning arrangement of contents. Bur 1656 (Aug.)-1657 (Jul.) are omitted from Ms 4311, but are included in Ms 4312.

Bap 1675-1783 (with St Mary Bothaw), mar 1672-1754 (with St Mary Bothaw), bur 1656-78 (tr of bur entries in Ms 4311, 1656-65; with St Mary Bothaw from c.1670), **Ms 4312**. Indexes: **in Webb 13** (bap and bur); **Boyd** (mar from 1726).

Bap 1784-1812 (with St Mary Bothaw), **Ms 4313**. Index: **in Webb 13**.

Mar 1754-1812, banns 1754-60, **Ms 4315**. Index: **Boyd** (except 1776-1800).

Bur 1678-1812 (with St Mary Bothaw), **Ms 4314**. Index: **in Webb 13**.

Bap 1813-1944, mar 1813-37, bur 1813-53 and 1935 (all with St Mary Bothaw), **Ms 4553**. Indexes: **in Webb 13** (bap to 1840, and bur); **in Webb 54/ 1-2** (bur); **Boyd** (mar).

Mar 1837-1941 (with St Mary Bothaw), **Ms 4554**.

Banns 1778-1852 (with St Mary Bothaw), **Ms 4317**, 3 vol.

1. 1778-99 2. 1800-23 3. 1824-52.

Index: **Boyd** (1801-37).

Transcripts:

Mar 1619-65 and 1672-1837, banns 1754-60 and 1778-1837, **Challen 31**.

Bap 1675-1840, bap 1841-91 of persons born before 1841, bur 1656-1853 and 1935, **Webb 13**. Indexed.

B tr of bap, mar and bur 1629-31, **in Ms 10107**; bap, mar and bur 1639-40, **in Ms 10107A**; bap 1800-34, 1836-50, 1852-75 and 1881-4, mar 1800-34, 1836-50, 1852-75 and 1881, bur 1800-34 and 1836-53 (all with St Mary Bothaw from 1813), **Ms 11345**.

ST THOMAS APOSTLE

United to St Mary Aldermary, 1670

Partial index to bap and mar in **IGI**.

Bap 1558-1679/80, mar 1558-1672, bur 1558-1679/80, **in Ms 9009**. Indexes: **Boyd** (mar); **in HS 6** (bap, mar and bur).

Bap and bur 1680-1704: no reg for these years is known to exist. It is probable that the reg has been lost, but possibly registrations for St Thomas Apostle are among those entered in the reg of St Mary Aldermary (Ms 8990/2), where the parish of origin of the persons baptised and buried is not stated.

Bap and bur 1704-1812, **Ms 9010**. Indexes: **in HS 6** (to 1754); **in Webb 8** (from 1754).

Bap 1813-73, **Ms 9011**. Index: **in Webb 8** (to 1840).

Mar 1672-1754: see St Mary Aldermary.

Mar 1754-75, banns 1754-68, **Ms 9012**. Index: **in Webb 8**.

Mar 1776-1812, **in Ms 8993**. Index: **in Webb 8**.

Mar 1813-35, **Ms 9013**. Index: **in Webb 8**.

Mar 1837-69, **Ms 9013A**.

Banns 1770-1873, **Ms 9015**.

Bur 1813-49, **Ms 9014**. Bur accounts 1813-38, **in Ms 4866** (recording causes of death). Index to Ms 9014: **in Webb 8 and 54/1-2**.

For later bap, mar and banns, and for mar licences from 1860, see St Mary Aldermary.

Transcripts:

Bap 1558-1679/80 and 1704-54, mar 1558-1672, bur 1558-1679/80 and 1704-54, **HS 6**. Indexed.

Bap 1754-1840, bap 1841-73 of persons born before 1841, mar 1754-1835, bur 1754-1849, **Webb 8**. Indexed.

B tr of bap, mar and bur 1639-39/40, **in Ms 10107A**; bap 1800-49, mar 1800-10 and 1813-35, bur 1800-49, **Ms 11494**.

ST THOMAS IN THE LIBERTY OF THE ROLLS

District chapelry constituted 1842; united to St Dunstan in the West, 1886

Partial index to bap and mar in **IGI**.

Bap 1842-58, **Ms 10362/1**. Index: **in Webb 3** (bap of persons born before 1841).

Bap 1858-86, **Ms 10362/2**. Index: **in Webb 3** (bap of persons born before 1841).

Mar 1845-85, **Ms 10363**.

ST VEDAST FOSTER LANE

Partial index to bap and mar in **IGI**.

Bap 1558-c.1940, mar 1559-1754, bur 1558-1812: reg damaged beyond repair by enemy action in 1940 and not available for use. The following sources are available:

> Tr and index of bap 1558-1836, mar 1559-1837, bur 1558-1837, **HS 29-30**. Mar also indexed in **Boyd**.
>
> B tr of bap, mar and bur 1799-1800, 1803-8 and 1810-12, held by Lambeth Palace Library, London SE1 7JU.
>
> B tr of bap 1813-59, **Ms 11252/1**. Index: **in Webb 102** (1837-40).
>
> Tr of bap 1882-96 (with St Michael le Querne, St Matthew Friday Street and St Peter Westcheap), **in Ms 10955**. Indexed.

Mar 1754-88, banns 1754-1809 (both with St Michael le Querne), **Ms 6495/1**. Indexes to mar: **Boyd**; **in HS 30**.

Mar 1789-1813 (with St Michael le Querne), **Ms 6495/2**. Indexes: **Boyd**; **in HS 30**.

Mar 1813-37, **Ms 6495/3**. Indexes: **Boyd**; **in HS 30**.

Mar 1838-c.1940: reg damaged beyond repair by enemy action in 1940 and not available for use. B tr of mar 1838-58, **Ms 11252/3**.

Mar 1954-68, **Ms 6495/4**.

Mar 1968-81, **Ms 6495/5**.

Bur 1813-53, **Ms 6496**. Indexes: **in HS 30** (to 1837); **in Webb 3** (1838-53); **in Webb 54/1-2**.

Later bap reg (from c.1940) retained by incumbent.

Transcripts:

Bap 1558-1836, **HS 29**. Indexed.

Mar 1559-1837, bur 1558-1837, **HS 30**. Indexed.

Bap 1837-40 (from b tr), **in Webb 102**. Indexed.

Bur 1838-53, **Webb 3**. Indexed.

B tr of bap 1813-59, **Ms 11252/1**; mar 1813-37, **Ms 11252/2**; mar 1838-58, **Ms 11252/3**; bur 1813-51, **Ms 11252/4**. Duplicate b tr of bap, mar and bur 1827-8, **Ms 11252/5**. Note: b tr of bap, mar and bur 1799-1800, 1803-8 and 1810-12 are held by Lambeth Palace Library, London SE1 7JU.

TEMPLE CHURCH

Partial index to bap and mar in **IGI**.

Reg (from 1628) held by the Master of the Temple, Master's House, Temple, London EC4Y 7BB.

Bap 1629-1853, mar 1628-1760, transcribed and indexed in **HS new series 1**. Mar 1701-60 indexed in **Boyd**.

Bur 1628/9-1853, transcribed and indexed in *Register of burials at the Temple church,* anon. (London, 1905), **GL Printed Books Section**. Bur 1813-53 indexed **in Webb 54/1-2**.

WHITEFRIARS PRECINCT

No separate reg maintained. Pre-1842 registrations for inhabitants of this precinct are found in the reg of St Bride Fleet Street and St Dunstan in the West. In 1842 the precinct was included in the district chapelry of Holy Trinity Gough Square, and from that date registrations should be sought in the reg of Holy Trinity and its parent parish, St Bride Fleet Street.

APPENDIX

Boyd's marriage index: Middlesex and London main series and Second and Third (Miscellaneous) series.

Boyd's marriage index comprises several county series and an additional Second and Third (Miscellaneous) series containing marriages from a number of counties. Guildhall Library holds a copy of the complete index in the Printed Books Section. The list given below provides details of the Anglican marriage registers of the City of London which are indexed in the Middlesex and London series and Second and Third (Miscellaneous) series. Readers should note that the index was made from transcripts, published and unpublished, not from original registers; that for some City parishes banns books as well as marriage registers have been indexed, but the index does not always indicate whether a particular entry relates to banns or to a marriage; and that the Middlesex and London series includes some apparently random entries for dates, parishes and counties beyond its listed scope. Variant spellings of surnames are standardised in the index, and these are not cross-referenced; but the method employed in standardisation is explained in *A list of parishes in Boyd's marriage index* (Society of Genealogists, 1994), a copy of which can be seen at the Printed Books enquiry desk.

Allhallows Bread Street 1538-1837
Allhallows Honey Lane 1546-1656, 1664-6 and 1818-36
Allhallows Lombard Street 1553-1837 and banns 1654-62/3, 1755-75 and 1801-37
Allhallows London Wall 1559-1675, 1701-75 and 1801-37 and banns 1823-37
Allhallows Staining 1653-1740, 1748-50 and 1753
Allhallows the Great 1671-1722/3, 1741/2-75 and 1801-37
Allhallows the Less 1558-1666
Bridewell chapel 1671-93 and 1701-25
Christchurch Newgate Street 1538-88 and 1667-1754
Fleet marriages, including some of the Mint, Southwark, c.1667-1754 (selective entries only: the majority of these mar remain unindexed)
Guildhall chapel 1668/9-84/5
Holy Trinity Minories 1579-1663
Holy Trinity the Less 1547-1753
Lamb's Chapel 1618-98
Mercers' Hall chapel 1701-54
St Andrew Hubbard 1538-1622
St Andrew Undershaft 1726-75 and 1801-37 and banns 1754-60, 1764-75, 1801-14 and 1824-37
St Antholin Budge Row 1538/9-1754
St Augustine Watling Street 1559-1775 and 1801-36[1] and banns 1754-75 and 1801-5
St Bartholomew by the Exchange 1558/9-1706 and 1712-54
St Benet Fink 1538/9-1775 and 1801-36 and banns 1653-62, 1699-1715, 1754-75 and 1801-36
St Benet Gracechurch 1558-1837 and banns 1754-75
St Benet Paul's Wharf 1619-1837
St Benet Sherehog c.1670-1837 and banns 1754-1837

St Botolph Aldersgate 1640-1755 and banns 1653-64
St Botolph Billingsgate 1685/6-1837
St Botolph Bishopsgate 1558-1754
St Christopher le Stocks 1557-1780 and banns 1755-80
St Clement Eastcheap 1539-1839 and banns 1801-30
St Dionis Backchurch 1538-1837 and banns 1754-75 and 1801-23
St Dunstan in the East 1605/6-25
St Dunstan in the West 1701-75 and (selectively) c.1801-12 and banns 1754-7
St Edmund the King 1673-1812
St Ethelburga Bishopsgate 1679-1754 and 1792-1837
St Faith under St Paul 1813-37[1]
St George Botolph Lane 1547-1837
St Giles Cripplegate 1561-1625
St Gregory by St Paul 1559-1754
St Helen Bishopsgate 1575-1837 and banns 1754-77
St James Duke's Place 1664-8 and 1678/9-1837
St James Garlickhithe 1708-54
St John the Evangelist Friday Street 1653-66
St Katherine Coleman 1563-1738 and 1741-54
St Lawrence Jewry 1538-1764
St Lawrence Pountney 1538/9-1666, 1715 and 1813-37 and banns 1654-9
St Leonard Eastcheap 1538-1705
St Magnus the Martyr 1557/8-1775 and 1801-37 and banns 1754-7 and 1801-37
St Margaret Lothbury 1558-1754
St Margaret Moses 1558-1666
St Margaret Pattens 1559-1660
St Martin Ludgate 1626-1700
St Martin Orgar 1625-1839 and banns 1801-30
St Martin Outwich 1670-1837 and banns 1755-76 and 1824-37
St Martin Pomeroy 1539-1647/8
St Martin Vintry 1675-1710
St Mary Abchurch 1558-1775 and 1801-37 and banns 1757-62
St Mary Aldermanbury 1701-21, 1751-75 and 1801-37
St Mary Aldermary 1558-1754
St Mary at Hill 1701-54
St Mary Bothaw 1754-75 and 1801-12 and banns 1754-64
St Mary Colechurch 1558-1665/6 and 1683/4-84
St Mary le Bow 1538-1631 and 1675-1837 and banns 1754-1837
St Mary Magdalen Milk Street 1559-1666
St Mary Magdalen Old Fish Street 1664-1754
St Mary Mounthaw 1568-1666, 1754-75 and 1801-35
St Mary Somerset 1558/9-1775 and 1801-37
St Mary Woolchurch Haw 1559-1666
St Mary Woolnoth 1538-1754
St Matthew Friday Street 1538-1775 and 1801-36
St Michael Bassishaw 1538-1764

St Michael Cornhill 1546-1650, 1701-75 and 1801-36 and banns 1745-75
St Michael Crooked Lane 1539-1775 and 1801-35 and banns 1745-75 and 1801-35
St Michael le Querne 1686-1705 and 1813-36
St Michael Paternoster Royal 1558-1775 and 1801-37
St Michael Queenhithe 1701-53
St Michael Wood Street 1745-1837
St Mildread Bread Street [2] 1670/1- 1837 and banns 1754-74
St Mildread Poultry [2] 1538-1754
St Nicholas Acons 1539-1664
St Nicholas Cole Abbey 1584-1812
St Olave Hart Street 1563-1754
St Olave Jewry 1538/9-1754
St Pancras Soper Lane 1538-1674 and 1818-36
St Paul's Cathedral 1697-1758
St Peter Cornhill 1538/9-1754
St Peter le Poer 1561-1775 and 1801-37 and banns 1755-75 and 1801-17
St Peter Paul's Wharf 1607-60, 1684, 1698-1704/5 and 1828-34
St Peter Westcheap 1538-1698/9 and 1814-36
St Sepulchre Holborn 1662-1754
St Stephen Coleman Street 1701-54
St Stephen Walbrook 1557-1837 and banns 1754-1837
St Swithin London Stone 1726-75 and 1801-37 and banns 1754-60 and 1801-37
St Thomas Apostle 1558-1754
St Vedast Foster Lane 1559-1837
Temple Church 1701-60

[1] mar from 1831 at St Augustine Watling Street and St Faith under St Paul are all indexed under 'St Augustine', but there are actually separate reg for each of the two parishes.

[2] this index frequently fails to distinguish between St Mildread Bread Street and St Mildred Poultry. Many mar are indexed under 'St Mildred', with no indication of which parish is meant; a number of others are assigned to the wrong parish.